RealAge®
Recipes

Michael F. Roizen, M.D., and **John La Puma, M.D.**

Reader's Digest

The Reader's Digest Association, Inc.
Pleasantville, NY / Montreal

The recipes and information in this book originally appeared in *Cooking the RealAge Way* and are published in this special edition, arranged by Reader's Digest, by permission of HarperCollins Publishers, 10 East 53rd Street, New York, NY 10022.

Library of Congress Cataloging-in-Publication Data has been applied for.
ISBN 0-7621-0717-0

Address any comments about *RealAge Recipes* to
The Reader's Digest Association, Inc.
Editor-in-Chief, Home & Health Books
Reader's Digest Road
Pleasantville, NY 10570-7000

To order copies of *RealAge Recipes*, call 1 800-846-2100.
Visit our Web site at rd.com

Printed in the United States of America

10 9 8 7 6 5 4 3 2 1

Cooking the
RealAge Way

*Control Your Genes Simply by
the Way You Set Up Your Kitchen*

You do not have to feel or be your calendar age. Seventy percent of premature aging is caused by the choices we make. By making some good choices, such as eating well, you can slow down or even reverse the signs of aging. And the best way to eat well is by revising key elements of the most important room in your home—the kitchen.

Just as what you eat makes a big difference in how old you feel and how old you actually are, it also amazingly makes a difference in what proteins your genes produce. As we learn more about genes, we learn how much we can modify their actions. The specific proteins they produce and the ratio of proteins any two genes make is at least partially under your control. This chapter is about how we can stock our kitchens and change what we eat to control our genes, ultimately keeping our families and us energetic and younger.

The response to *The RealAge Makeover*, which provides consistent scientific data that you can control your rate of aging, has been overwhelming. Thousands of e-mails have told me that knowing the effect of a healthy choice—for example, knowing that eating an ounce of nuts a day makes the average 55-year-old man more than 3.3 years younger—is empowering. Such knowledge motivated individuals to make healthier choices. People tell me they love having a way of measuring their rate of aging and, even better, have found some simple steps for slowing that process.

Consistent scientific data show that eating the RealAge way—great-tasting, healthy food that is colorful—can make you younger. The scientific advisory group of RealAge has a strict standard to follow: no food choice (and no other health factor, for that matter) is said to have a RealAge effect (e.g., "Enjoying a half-ounce of dark—cocoa based—chocolate before each meal can make you 1.9 years younger") unless that effect has been shown to occur in at least four studies on humans. In addition, each RealAge food choice should be (and is, as confirmed by taste tests) every bit as satisfying and delicious as the energy-sapping, aging foods so widespread in the American diet. My patients and readers love knowing that simple, easy changes in food choices make a measurable difference in their health.

This is where cooking the RealAge way comes in. Perhaps a patient story helps: Steve I. was a 52-year-old hard-driving executive. His wife, Nancy, cared deeply about him, so when he was home for dinner (he ate out or was away two or three nights every week), Nancy cooked his favorite roasts or steaks. She punctuated every meal with great vegetables and a good salad, but Nancy always had his favorite coffee ice cream (to make him feel like home was a comfortable spot); and on planes or on the road he ate whatever was being served (he traveled in first class often, owing to his frequent-flier status); Mrs. Field's cookies and ice cream for dessert were rewards. And he ate whatever everybody else was eating at meetings. He and his wife exercised two or three times a week when he was at home. But he was getting more tired, enjoying the work less, and his arthritis started to act up. So his wife forced him to see me.

We found his RealAge was thirteen years older than his calendar age; he was really 65, not 52, and he felt it. So he made small changes that made a big difference. Just changing to nuts and chocolate-covered fruit as a snack, ordering fish or vegetarian meals in advance on planes, asking for olive oil, throwing the creamy dressings out, and stocking the kitchen with a balsamic vinegar he adored, his wife making RealAge dishes he loved, and prioritizing 20 minutes of exercise a day, he transformed himself easily into someone who felt 45 not 65. Actually, he became 45 (his RealAge decreased to 45 over three years). He became vigorous and regained his zest for life, and he looked it. So did his wife, who became transformed as well.

And it was easy, they say. It started by understanding why we feel and get older, and how easy it is to deliciously transform our eating. It just started and was (and is) done with easy changes in the kitchen. Nancy looked and felt younger, too. Steve and she each lost weight (18 and 9 pounds, respectively), but that was not their goal. They wanted to feel the zest for life and energy that had gradually slipped away. They wanted the energy to help their children build families and to enjoy their grandchildren. They just didn't know how easy it was; neither did I until I started to learn about how we can control our genes—how solid that science was—that started for me more than twenty years after I was a doctor, and more than ten years ago.

Now many of us wish we could be 9 or 18 pounds lighter, or feel and be twenty years younger. And we can. That it is easy and predictable is the great news. Steve and Nancy's story is not unique and their transformation is not unusual or different. Many others (myself and my wife included) have done it. And it is not even hard; it is even fun. I want you to learn what I've learned—it's too easy and too important not to learn it. *The RealAge Makeover* reveals the scientific principles and strategies to help you make yourself younger. Its goal is to help you understand the science behind control of your genes. This book applies these concepts to preparation of food—how to cook food so it tastes great and makes your RealAge younger. Reading this book and cooking the RealAge way is an easy way to look, feel, and be at least five to eight years and probably fourteen years younger than your calendar age.

I'm a medical doctor and a research scientist. My co-author, John La Puma, is also a medical doctor, as well as a professionally trained chef. We take enormous pride in knowing that the RealAge concepts have helped so many people add extra, vigorous, quality-filled years to their lives. It's not just about living longer. It's about enjoying a higher quality of life at all ages.

Unfortunately, too many of us have come to think of cooking and eating in the wrong way. We eat food out of habit and convenience, instead of making our meals a joyful focal point in our lives. Instead of celebrating food, we feel ambivalent about it. Time spent sharing a meal with loved ones should be a celebration. Food nourishes us, sustains us, makes us grow, and gives us energy. It is a positive force in our lives, making us feel good, alive, and younger every day. Grow old gracefully? Not you. You'll live life to your youngest!

With some effort and a little practice, you can create RealAge-smart and energy-giving meals that are as delicious as those created by a top chef but without all the cream and butter. But before you learn how, you might want to know something about the RealAge concept and a little of the science behind it. Then you'll understand how much you can control how well and how long you will live.

The RealAge Concept

If you've read *The RealAge Makeover* already, you are familiar with the RealAge concept, which states that the fundamental source of your overall good health is the good maintenance of two of the most important systems in the body: the cardiovascular system (the heart and blood vessels) and the immune system. While we do not know the molecular basis of aging, we do know what ages. The aging of your arteries is responsible for such potentially disabling conditions as strokes, heart attacks, memory loss, impotence, decay in the quality of orgasm, and wrinkling of your skin. And aging of the other major system, the immune system, can lead to autoimmune diseases, such as arthritis; to serious infections, such as pneumonia; and to cancer. RealAge identifies what factors are important in your aging processes for these systems, how you can change those factors to keep yourself younger, and the relative value of such choices. For example, eating an ounce of nuts a day keeps the average 55-year-old man 3.3 years younger. Similarly, consuming less than 20 grams of saturated and trans fats a day makes the average 55-year-old woman 2.7 years younger. RealAge is really like money: it places a value on your choices. There are many choices you can make to keep your arteries and immune system younger.

The good news is that to a large extent we do not have to be at the mercy of fate or heredity. Seventy percent of premature aging is caused by the choices we make. By making some easy choices, you can slow—or even reverse—aging, regardless of your inherited genetics. The choices that can easily make you younger include food choices.

Getting Back to the Basics

A walk down the aisle of any grocery store will reveal the predominance of foods high in the kinds of fat that age you (not all fat ages you), and in simple sugars and salt. Although this quickly reveals the extent to which the quality of the average American diet has declined, it also shows to what extent most of us have forgotten, or have never experienced, the most fundamental pleasures of cooking and enjoying our kitchens.

The existence of prepared mixes for bread machines is a perfect example. To make bread in a bread machine, you measure flour, water, yeast, milk, and salt and then press a button. Nothing could be simpler. However, the fact that Nancy (of Steve and Nancy above) served her family bread made in this machine with a commercially packaged mix that is full of added chemicals, stabilizers, and sodium—just to save the time necessary for collecting and measuring ingredients—shows the extent to which many of us feel too busy to spend time measuring, pouring, and mixing in our own kitchens. Nancy just didn't know. She did care. Probably this predominance of packaged food is partly due to the prevalence of busier-than-ever two-career families. Many busy working people regard grocery shopping and cooking as just two more chores at the end of a stress-filled day. This need not be the case. Armed with a "smart" kitchen—one that has the right ingredients and equipment—and an understanding of simple cooking techniques, you can quickly and easily create a great-tasting, healthy, and energy-giving meal. How you stock your kitchen can result in a high IQ: a kitchen with a high IQ is smart enough to help control your genes and make your RealAge younger.

Like everything else that is important in life, learning to change habits, such as switching from aging to age-reducing food choices, takes a little dedication and persistence. In a short time, your new RealAge-smart habits will become such a natural part of your life that you'll wonder how you ever lived any other way. Learning how to cook and how to enjoy a great-tasting, RealAge-smart meal will take some practice, it's true. But you wouldn't expect to break 90 on your first day on the golf course. Similarly, it will take time to retrain your taste buds (a key to enjoying great-tasting food). Soon, however, your RealAge dishes will taste better than the artery-aging bucket of greasy fried chicken or the energy-sapping take-out food you would have chosen. I know because I, too, had to work to change bad eating habits. It was also challenging for a doctor whose food specialty was toast to learn how to cook. But now I'm full of energy, I keep my weight at a steady low level, and best of all, I've made myself younger—and I enjoy the extra vitality.

The Science Behind the Numbers

If you chart the health, longevity, and, ultimately, youth of a "population age cohort"—a group of people all born in the same year—you will find that, with few exceptions, people age at a similar rate until they reach their late twenties or mid-thirties. With the exception of those who have inherited rare genetic disorders or have been in serious accidents, everyone is basically healthy and able. Men reach the peak of their performance curve in their late twenties, women in their mid-thirties. At that time, our bodies have fully matured, and we are at our strongest and most mentally acute. Then, somewhere between 28 and 36 years of age, most people reach a turning point, a transition from "growing" into "aging."

If you examine the population as a whole and track any one biological function—be it kidney function or cognitive ability—performance declines as we age. In general, after the age of 35, each biological function decreases about 5 percent every ten years. That decrease is a measure of the average for the population as a whole. Although these kinds of measurements have been the standards used by scientists to calculate the rate of aging, the averages don't take into account variation between individuals. The variation is so great among people over 40 that it is often meaningless to calculate an average at all. Averages are statistically meaningful only if the values for the people or things being measured actually congregate closely around the midpoint (that is, if everyone is pretty much the same).

When we age, there is so much variation between individuals over age 40 that the "average" obscures more than it shows. Rather than gathering around a mean (the midpoint), there are people in every age group who manifest every level of functioning. Some show dramatic decline, others show virtually no decline. What you eat contributes mightily to this difference between people. Twins who choose different lifestyles or foods age at different rates. People with genetic diseases such as type 2 diabetes can age at different rates if they make different choices.

Our genes matter. Genes simply make proteins—that is how genes cause their effects. But how much of each protein a gene makes changes as we grow older and the ratio of some proteins to other proteins changes as we grow older. But changing what we eat, for example from red meat to fish, might change the ratio of proteins from that typical of an older person to one typical of a younger person. Feeding your genes more B_6, B_{12}, and folate may make them less vulnerable to chromosome breaks or substitutions. This type of change in what your genes produce or how they function with a change in your habits exemplifies the control you can exert over your genes and the diseases that are characteristic of aging. And you do not have to memorize long lists—it is easy to put it into everyday choices.

First, a Little Science
Aging of the Arteries

Keeping your arteries young and healthy is the single most important thing you can do for your health. Simply put, you're as young as your arteries. When your arteries are not taken care of properly—for example, when your diet is high in saturated or trans fats—they get clogged with fatty buildup, diminishing the amount of oxygen and nutrients that can get to the cells.

There are four major types of dietary fat: saturated, polyunsaturated, monounsaturated, and trans fat. The first three occur naturally. The fourth, trans fat, is usually an artificially created product that mimics saturated fat. Trans fat—also called trans fatty acid—is created when unsaturated fats are hydrogenated (combined with hydrogen). The purpose of this chemical process is to create fats that are solid at room temperature rather than liquid, their normal state at room temperature. For example, most solid margarine is produced by transforming (through partial hydrogenation) good vegetable oils into bad vegetable oils. Even though a food label doesn't use the exact words "trans fat," if you see "partially hydrogenated vegetable oils" or "hydrogenated oils" as an ingredient, you can be sure the product contains trans fat. Any fat that is liquid when heated but hardens when cooled to room temperature is probably made of either saturated or trans fat. If the fat is solid when cool, it will age you. For example, most stick margarine is trans fat, as is much of the glaze on doughnuts.

Since food producers are not required to list trans fats on their nutrition labels, trans fat is called "the hidden fat." The FDA has announced that the trans fat content of food must be listed on labels by 2006. Some food manufacturers are not pleased with this requirement. Many packaged foods—cookies, crackers, and chips—contain these oils because they give food a longer shelf life (and you a shorter life filled with more disability). Many cookies and crackers claim to be "baked, not fried," or to have "no saturated fat" or "no cholesterol." This implies they're low in fat, when in fact they're often full of trans fat. It doesn't matter if the product is cholesterol-free; if it contains trans fat, it will age your arteries and immune system.

When your arteries get clogged with fatty buildup, not only your cardiovascular system but also your entire body ages more quickly. Cardiovascular disease, which is brought on by aging of the arteries, is the major cause of heart attacks, strokes, many types of kidney disease, and memory loss. Even mild forms of vascular disease that won't actually kill you can sap your energy and make you feel old and tired.

Aging of the arteries also causes impotence, diminished quality of orgasm, and even wrinkling of the skin.

Luckily, small, easy-to-make changes in food choices and in lifestyle can profoundly improve your arterial health and can reverse a great deal of the aging that has already taken place. Simply eating certain foods, such as a little garlicky olive oil in a pasta dish or a great-tasting tomato sauce, can reduce the fatty arterial-wall buildup that can lead to vascular disease. More than six studies in the highest-quality peer-reviewed medical literature have reported that both garlic and olive oil decrease aging of the arteries, and that the two, eaten together regularly, can make you over three years younger if you're a 50-year-old man or two years younger if you're a 50-year-old woman. What's more, garlic and olive oil taste great.

These foods can also decrease the likelihood that a cell will have a break in its DNA that could lead to cancer. That's right; just switching from one fat (butter or margarine) to another (olive or nut oil) can make your arteries and immune system many years younger.

Aging of the Immune System

In addition to taking care of your arteries, don't let your immune system make you old. As you age, your immune system begins to get sloppy, ignoring important warning signals and becoming negligent. You can end up with cancer or another disorder caused by a malfunction of the immune system. For example, when you are young—except in relatively rare cases—genetic controls in your cells protect your cells from becoming cancerous. If one of these cellular controls slips up, all is not lost. Your larger immune system can identify precancerous cells in the body and eliminate them. Thus, your body has a double block against cancer, one on the cellular level and one on the organism-wide level.

As you age, both the cell-based genetic controls and your immune system become more likely to malfunction, and you are more likely to develop a cancerous tumor. Also, many types of arthritis are examples of a breakdown of the immune system, which is why arthritis is another disease associated with aging. Luckily, some food choices, such as having a bowl of fresh mixed berries as an afternoon snack, can help your body shed free radicals (substances that can cause cell damage), which lessens your chance of getting arthritis, macular degeneration (a disease that destroys vision), and even cancer. (Nature got it right: the best foods are almost always the most naturally delicious and the most colorful.) The RealAge kitchen program also helps reduce the stress in your life; stress can upset the balance of the immune system.

Getting Younger with Lycopene

The tomato-sauce story is even more important to aging, and even more scientifically solid than the garlic–olive oil story. There are more than thirty studies in humans showing that consumption of 10 tablespoons of tomato sauce a week decreases the likelihood of cancer. Breast and prostate cancer are the two cancers for which the most evidence exists for prevention of cancer by consumption of tomato sauce or, more precisely, lycopene, the carotenoid in tomato sauce that is believed to be the active ingredient for health. Although lycopene is also found in guava, watermelon, and pink grapefruit, it is most easily absorbed from cooked tomatoes combined with a little oil.

Although we do not use test-tube data when calculating a RealAge effect— we use only data from studies on human beings—it should be noted that the addition of lycopene (from tomatoes) to human cells in test tubes and cell cultures has decreased the number of breaks that occur in DNA. Such breaks are thought to be the precursors of cancer. So, in addition to a substantial amount of data in human beings that tomato sauce decreases the risk of cancer, biologic evidence from test tubes gives us a mechanism for the effect. These data may not thrill your taste buds, but tomatoes can. Having 10 table-spoons of tomato sauce a week makes the typical 55-year-old man 1.9 years younger and the typical 55-year-old woman 0.7 years younger.

There may be a bonus to keeping your RealAge younger with lycopene, whatever the source. As of this writing, three studies in humans have shown that lycopene is associated with an impressive reversal, or slowing, of aging of the arteries. Because we must have four supporting studies in humans before we claim that a factor produces an effect on RealAge, we cannot say that con-sumption of lycopene decreases aging of the arteries. If, however, the data from these three studies are corroborated in a fourth study, that will increase tomato's RealAge effect, making 10 tablespoons a week of tomato sauce give you a three-year benefit. Eating tomato sauce is a pretty easy and delicious way to make your RealAge younger, don't you think? And maybe realizing just that— that it was easy and fun to make yourself more than half a year younger—is why it's so enjoyable to make a few RealAge-smart choices.

How to Implement the RealAge Concept in Your Kitchen

The Goals of RealAge

Learning to live the RealAge way is like learning to do anything—riding a bike, using a computer, reading. Practice and a little coaching go a long way. Changing your kitchen habits and your eating habits (and other food-related habits, such as cooking regularly at home or being a smarter grocery shopper) requires just a little time and just a little consistency. If you aren't used to cooking healthy meals for your family, it isn't second nature. But to make healthy eating an enjoyable, natural part of your life, you just have to take the first step. It's easier and more fun than you ever imagined!

The goal of increasing your kitchen IQ and RealAge cooking is age reduction—giving you a higher quality of life and more vigor every day. Weight reduction is a side effect of this diet that many find an unexpected bonus. However, feeling better every day, and feeling the power of more energy every day, are the benefits patients tell me I can guarantee if you cook the RealAge way for ninety days.

Making Every Calorie Delicious and Nutrient-Rich

If you are aware of the amount of saturated and trans fat you consume and make everything you eat nutrient-rich, calorie-poor, and delicious, it will be hard for you to gain weight unless you are malnourished. It will be easy to maintain or lose weight.

You won't go far astray if you remember the RealAge mantra: whenever you eat, make every calorie delicious and nutrient-rich. Learn the pleasure of spending time in a well-stocked, RealAge-smart kitchen, or what we call a "high-IQ kitchen." Include your friends and loved ones, so that you have the pleasure of their company and, at the same time, the satisfaction of seeing them become more vibrant and energized as a result of the healthy foods you're serving them.

The food choices of the average American are responsible for approximately one-third of his or her rate of aging. Other choices, which are discussed in *The RealAge Makeover*, determine the other two-thirds of the rate of aging: stress, group participation, family history, job choices, physical activities, and good and bad habits, such as flossing, wearing a helmet when you bike, or smoking. Regularly eating nutrient-poor, calorie-rich choices such as Cinnabons, Bloomin' Onions, or Cheesecake Factory Carrot Cake can make your RealAge as much as thirteen years older than your calendar age. In contrast, eating delicious foods that are nutrient-rich can make you years younger than your calendar age. Every item you choose to eat should be world class in taste and nutrients. If you choose great-tasting foods that are full of vitamins, minerals, nutrients, and fiber rather than empty calories, you're eating the RealAge way.

My friends have asked me to summarize the principles of RealAge cooking on a card or foldover set of sheets they could carry in their breast pocket or purse for the first ninety days. The following 27 points are those principles, followed by a brief explanation of each.

Eating the RealAge Way

If you follow these practices, your food choices can make your RealAge 14 years younger:

1 Make every calorie you eat delicious and nutrient-rich.
Don't eat foods that taste just "okay." If they're not special, don't let them touch your lips. You deserve to treat yourself well.

2 Eat foods that aren't processed.
If you rarely eat packaged goods or prepared foods, you'll usually know what's in your food.

3 Eat breakfast—preferably, a whole grain and a little healthy fat.
You'll start the day off with energy, avoid hunger pangs that lead to unwise food choices, and have more stable blood sugar levels. Try real peanut butter on toasted rye or on a chewy whole wheat bagel, or a Kashi cereal.

4 Eat some healthy fat first at every meal.
The ideal amount represents approximately 60–75 calories: 1/2 tablespoon of olive oil or canola oil, 6 walnuts, 12 almonds, 20 peanuts, or 1/2 ounce of cocoa-based chocolate or avocado.

5   Read the labels for serving size.

Determine exactly how many servings you will be eating, and how many grams of saturated and trans fat that amount contains. Avoid products that put you over your daily limit of 20 grams, or that have more than 6 grams in a serving you'll eat.

6   Read the labels for whole-grain content.

Look at the first six items in the label. The first that involves grains should say "whole wheat," "oats," "oats, unprocessed," "brown rice," "corn," etc. Choose products that have more whole-grain content than processed-grain content.

7   Tally your saturated and trans fat consumption every day.

Try to keep it to less than 20 grams a day. No matter what the special interest lobbyists say, eating more than 20 grams a day of saturated and trans fat (we call these two together the "Aging Fats"; see earlier in this chapter) correlates with the development of arterial aging (heart disease, stroke, memory loss, impotence, decay in orgasm quality, wrinkling of the skin) and cancer (the evidence is strongest for increases in saturated and trans fats being associated with the development of breast and prostate cancers). And aging fats sap your energy acutely when they prevent your arteries from dilating as your muscles need more oxygen. The risk of arterial disease and cancer seems to increase substantially as your intake of saturated and trans fats combined exceeds 20 grams a day.

8   Limit red meat consumption to 4 ounces a week.

This includes "the other white meat." Use red meat as a side dish or condiment, not a main course.

9   Read the label when you buy baked goods.

Choose those with whole grains, and no aging trans or saturated fats, and great texture. Baked goods tend to make you older because they contain tons of trans fats and processed flour. One Cinnabon, I'm told, contains 75 grams of aging fat—not a four-pack, but just one

Cinnabon; a slice of whole-grain cinnamon-flavored bread made by our local Montana Bread Company or by P & C contains no aging or other fat and no processed flour, tastes great, and if you want to make it even healthier, add some peanut butter or pure avocado spread.

10 Substitute healthier foods.

Assess your foods and meals in terms of how they could be made healthier by additions, subtractions, or substitutions. A few substitutions can make a big difference in your rate of aging. They also make food taste great! Try substituting olive oil for butter or margarine on bread, or prune puree or drained applesauce for 1 to 3 tablespoons of butter in smaller recipes; fruit for cookies; real (dark) chocolate for milk chocolate; nuts for chips; and cooked garlic salsa or marinara sauce for a cream sauce.

11 Make eating, and the place you eat, special.

Only eat sitting down at one of your special places. (Usually, designate no more than three places as "special"—one at home and perhaps two at work). Only eat food on plates and on 9-inch plates, not giant ones. My most successful patients (and their families) have a special place in their home that is the only place for eating. Not eating anyplace else was and is their rule—not the TV room, not standing up, not in the car, not out of the refrigerator.

12 Take a 30-minute walk every day with a friend.

I call this a RealAge double dip. Not only do you get the anti-aging benefit that physical activity and exercise give you, but also you build the strong social support networks that can help you prevent needless aging through times of stress.

13 Plan menus and learn to cook.

Cooking can be a true pleasure; in addition, you will know what's in your food, and you will also have the fun of learning how to use herbs and spices to make food taste fabulous.

14 Be a smart shopper.

If you don't buy food that's bad for you, you won't eat food that's bad for you.

15 Eat nonfried fish three times a week.

Any fish, not just fatty fish, makes you younger.

16 Eat 10 tablespoons of tomato sauce a week.

Try marinara sauce, salsa, and other varieties. The carotenoid found in tomatoes, watermelon, guava, and pink grapefruit—lycopene—when eaten with a little oil, provides an immune-strengthening antioxidant that seems to inhibit growth of prostate, breast cancers, and maybe other cancers, and may make your arteries younger.

17 Add variety to your diet and the way you cook vegetables.

Why is variety in your diet so important? Many people don't eat a balanced diet. Forty percent of Americans don't eat fruit daily, and 30 percent don't consume any dairy or soy products regularly. On average, Americans get less than half of the 25 to 30 grams of fiber they need a day. Eating a diverse diet that is low in calories and high in nutrients decreases aging from arterial and immune dysfunction and makes your RealAge as much as four years younger. If you eat from all five food groups daily, you can be as much as five years younger than if you ate from only two. (The five groups are whole-grain breads and cereals; fruits; vegetables; dairy and dairy-substitute products; and meats, nuts, legumes, and other proteins). Adding variety to the way you cook will make all vegetables taste better, great even. It's also more fun to try new ways of cooking—and that makes you younger.

18 Be the CEO every time you eat out—why should you pay for something that ages you?

Learn to ask questions of the wait-staff when you eat out. Then learn to ask for healthy, great-tasting choices—"Would you ask the chef to substitute the marinara sauce for the Alfredo sauce?"

19 Keep your portions energy-giving, not energy-sapping.

The usual restaurant entrée is not an acceptable meal size. Use your fist or a pack of cards as a measure of a serving.

20 Stop eating as soon as you start to feel full.

Because your stomach is roughly the size of your fist, eating meals larger than your fist can stretch your stomach beyond what's comfortable or healthy. Eat a little healthy fat first. Then pause before the rest of the meal. And remember: stop eating as soon as you first sense you might be getting full—before the full feeling hits.

21 Don't eat absentmindedly.

All too often, eating is an unconscious act. We lift the fork, swallow absentmindedly, and lift the fork again. Sometimes we overeat because we just aren't paying attention. We're bored, nervous, or busy. Often, we're not even hungry. Instead, eat mindfully. Be actively conscious of what you're eating and why. Use all of your senses to enjoy the color, texture, smell, and flavor of your food. Not only will you enjoy your food more, but you'll also slow down your rate of consumption.

22 Do resistance exercises for 10 minutes every other day.

You replace a pound of your muscle with a pound of fat about every five years after age 35 if you do not do resistance exercises. And a pound of muscle uses about 150 calories a day, compared to 3 calories a day for a pound of fat. Whether you use free weights, resistance bands, or machines, it takes just 10 minutes three times a week to maintain muscle mass. (You can go to www.realage.com/realage-café/myfitnessplan to see these resistance exercises and design a plan for yourself, but I recommend consultation with a trainer for at least the first three times you do resistance exercises and then at least once every three months thereafter.)

23 Be a savvy snacker.

Think nutrient rich and calorie lean. Try a few nuts and a piece of whole fruit. Try not to snack at night.

24 Avoid simple carbohydrates and simple sugars.

Remember that carbohydrates were meant to be complex. Simple sugars in food are absorbed quickly in the intestine and increase the amount of sugar in the blood for at least one to two hours. A high concentration of sugar in the blood eradicates the natural protective control your body has over the usual, everyday variations in blood pressure. High blood-sugar levels also increase triglyceride levels in the blood.

What about honey and natural sugars? Unfortunately, these are not healthy substitutes for white sugar. So avoid foods that are laden with carbohydrates from brown sugar, corn sweetener, dextrose, fructose (high-fructose corn sweetener), glucose, corn syrup, honey, invert sugar, lactose, maltose, malt syrup, molasses, raw sugar, sucrose, syrup, and table sugar.

25 Drink alcohol in moderation.

Women benefit from one drink a day; men, from one or two. Avoid making this choice if you or your family are at risk of alcohol or drug abuse.

26 Drink lots of water.

Drink a glass of water between every glass of wine or other alcoholic drink you have. Also, at food events, carry a glass of water in one hand.

27 Take the right vitamins and minerals twice a day and avoid the wrong ones.

Find out what vitamins you should consider taking and in what amounts.

The
RealAge
Pantry

This chapter discusses the key principle of the RealAge pantry: "Easy Availability Begets Eating": that is, the first appealing thing you see is the first thing you'll eat. So, make the first appealing thing you see in your pantry a great-tasting healthy food. With a well-stocked RealAge pantry, you will always have a giant menu of delicious and healthy possibilities right at hand.

The secret to making your RealAge younger when you eat is to plan ahead. Have foods on hand that taste delicious and make you younger. If you don't have bad food choices on hand, you won't be tempted to eat them. So, go through your pantry and eliminate any food that doesn't fit a RealAge lifestyle. The more hydrogenated or saturated fat it has, the less healthy it is. Easy availability begets eating. The more fruits, vegetables, whole grains, legumes, fish, nuts, and seeds on hand, the better.

How you stock your pantry makes all the difference to your RealAge. Have you ever opened a cabinet door for a snack and found a Pop Tart staring at you? Or leftover holiday cookies? Chances are, you didn't close the door and grab a piece of fruit.

Simply put, if you keep RealAge-smart food choices on hand, you'll choose to eat them. You can be tempted by such RealAge-smart choices as dried fruit, Mexican salsa, whole wheat crackers, Kalamata olives, red peppers, or your favorite nuts.

The Well-Stocked RealAge Pantry

Stock up on the items listed here. Most don't need refrigeration and usually aren't canned or processed (the key exceptions are beans, tofu, tomatoes, and chiles), so RealAge-smart foods also do not have a lot of unwanted preservatives. Start small. Add just one new item to your grocery cart the first week—one you know you'll like and use. Next week, add one or two more.

Food	Uses
Applesauce	➤ A good snack and a great replacement for fat in recipes for baked goods. To concentrate its goodness for baking, drain applesauce in a coffee filter or folded paper towel. To avoid added sugar and chemicals, select the unsweetened, organic kind.
Arrowroot	➤ A thickening agent used for sauces, puddings, and other foods. Like cornstarch, it should be mixed with a liquid before being added to foods. Mix the arrowroot with a little of the liquid

Food	Uses

you're thickening, and then add this mixture a little later, when the soup, sauce, or stew is bubbling. As with cornstarch, the liquid must come to a boil for a few seconds for thickening to occur. We prefer arrowroot to cornstarch because arrowroot disappears into sauces and leaves nothing behind. However, cornstarch is more widely available and is much less expensive.

Artichoke hearts
➤ The tender center of the artichoke. Artichoke hearts are usually packed in an oil marinade or in water. Toss them with dried thyme and lemon juice for salads and pasta. They are delicious, low in calories, but rich in fiber, potassium, and calcium. Top pizzas with halved or quartered artichoke hearts straight from the jar.

Baking powder
➤ A leavening agent essential for making quickbreads (muffins, breads, scones). Always have a can in your pantry.

Baking soda
➤ A leavening agent for baked goods. Needs to be combined with an acid for the soda to work. As with baking powder, keep baking soda in your pantry, as some quickbread recipes will require it.

Beans and other legumes (black beans; garbanzo beans; kidney beans; lentils; pinto beans; pink, red, and white beans; split peas)
➤ Legumes include peas, lentils, and beans. Their high fiber and high protein content make them a healthy pleasure. They also come in a variety of beautiful colors. I especially love Anasazi beans, which cook faster than black beans and have a richer flavor and an interesting pink and white color. Include beans in soups and chili, blend them with garlic and chiles for dips, and combine them with tomatoes and peppers for a main course.

Food	Uses
Broth or stock (beef, chicken, fish, and vegetable broth or stock; clam juice)	➤ Needed for many recipes, broth adds flavor without adding fat or (usually) salt. Two large cans or boxes of reduced-salt broth in the pantry will expand your flavor possibilities. When a recipe calls for water, try using broth instead. The flavor will be richer and more complex, and you'll also be getting more vitamins and minerals. Remember: you can't use broth or stock for sautéing, as steaming, poaching, or simmering results instead.
Capers	➤ Little pickled flower buds from a shrub that grows only in the Mediterranean. Capers add a sharp, salty flavor to vinaigrettes, salads, pasta, and fish. For a tasty, healthy pâté, try pureeing capers with roasted red peppers, caramelized onions, and roasted garlic.
Cereal, dried	➤ Be sure to have oatmeal and whole rolled oats (not the instant, precooked kind) on hand. Then try corn flakes, raisin bran, Toasted O's, or even granolas that contain no hydrogenated fat (a granola made with olive oil is great). These are chock-full of healthy vitamins and fiber that make you younger. These can be used as toppings for yogurt and ice cream, as an easy snack, or for making cookies and breads. Experiment until you find a dried cereal you like—one that doesn't contain a lot of refined sugar and chemicals and does contain lots of fiber and vitamins.
Chiles (peppers)	➤ Available in many varieties, dried red peppers are all worth trying, as they taste great and are rich in flavonoids that make you younger. Try ancho chiles (dried poblano chiles that taste a little like oranges), chipotle chiles (dried, smoked jalapeño peppers), guajillo chiles (meaty), habanero chiles (extremely floral and fruity flavor, very hot, and often pickled), and pasilla chiles (long, thin, and fragrant). Look for chiles that are soft, not brittle. To decrease the heat and bring out the real flavor, discard the seeds and membranes, and then toast the chiles ever so slightly under a broiler. Or buy canned chipotles in a thick, spicy tomatoey adobo sauce, just to sample them.

Food	Uses
Cooking oil spray	➤ Eliminates the need to pour oil in your pan to coat it. The spray helps control the amount of fat you're using. Use olive oil or infused, cold-pressed canola oil in a mister or spray bottle. To make the oil go further, spread it on the pan with a paper towel.
Cornmeal	➤ A "whole" grain that can be a main ingredient in breads, muffins, pancakes, polenta, tamales, and tortillas. Buy it coarsely ground for hearty polenta, and finely ground for mixing into pancakes. Cornmeal can also be sprinkled on the bottom of pans to prevent quickbreads and pizzas from sticking.
Couscous	➤ Although couscous is just wheat, we've listed it separately from all the other grains because it's so easy to use. Still rolled by hand in many parts of Africa, couscous cooks instantly and takes on the flavor of whatever it's soaked or simmered in. We like it with spicy V8 juice, cilantro, and red onion. You might also like it with currants and dried cherries, simmered in white grape juice for just a minute, and topped with cracked macadamia nuts. Whatever you soak it in, couscous is a winner.
Dijon mustard	➤ Commercial yellow mustard is fine to have in your kitchen (I like the squeeze bottles), but if you want to add special flavor, use Dijon mustard, either smooth or whole-grain. Its tangy bite enlivens sandwiches and salad dressings and gives a kick to root vegetables, whole-grain breads, and hot dogs—tofu, turkey, or all beef!
Evaporated nonfat (skim) milk	➤ Has about 60 percent of the water removed and is a low-fat form of milk. You can use this product in baking and cream sauces, which will keep your RealAge younger.
Flour	➤ Used in baking and to coat pans or to prevent sticking when rolling out dough. For general cooking and baking, buy an all-purpose, unbleached, unbromated wheat flour—organic, if possible. (Check the label for those terms.) Avoid bromates!

Food	Uses
	Bromates, a chemical group used to strengthen bread dough, can be toxic and cancer-promoting and can make you older. Add other varieties of flour (for example, whole wheat) for specific recipes.
Fruits, dried	➤ Have some dried fruit for a light snack, mixed with yogurt, or baked into healthier scones. Toss some in a salad and mix some into oatmeal. Be careful, however: fruit can be very caloric when dried—a little goes a long way. Try whole figs, dates, prunes, raisins (several kinds—golden, Thompson, red flame), cranberries, cherries, currants, blueberries, and strawberries. Select organic dried fruit whenever possible.
Garlic	➤ Garlic is a joy because it complements almost anything. Gilroy, California, "The Garlic Capital of the World," even boasts a garlic ice cream. Garlic enhances fish and shellfish, pasta and grains, poultry and meats. Roast unpeeled foil-wrapped heads of garlic (45 minutes at 375°F is a starting point, as each oven is different) and squeeze out the pulp for a sweet spread for bread and crackers, a flavorful RealAge alternative to butter and margarine (maybe not right before you go to work!).
Ginger	➤ Fresh ginger can be sliced, diced, and chopped. It's great in marinades, stir-fried dishes, soups, vegetables, and ginger-bread. Look for a smooth, papery skin. If the root is shriveled or sprouting, pass it up: it's drying out and may have lost most of its juice. Ginger will last about two weeks when stored in a cool, dark, airy place.
Grains, whole (arborio rice, barley, brown rice, bulgur, millet, oats, quinoa, wild rice)	➤ Having several types of grains on hand can simplify meal preparation. Grains are easy to prepare and can be eaten alone, mixed with seasoning, or cooked in combination with other foods. Arborio, a short-grain rice, is usually used for making risotto because it releases starch quickly and makes the dish extra creamy. Barley is used in breads, cereals, and soups.

Food	Uses
	Brown rice, which is rice that has not had its husks removed, is rich in fiber and can be used in any dish calling for white rice. Bulgur is wheat that has been steamed and cracked into grits; it's commonly used for tabbouleh, a classic Mediterranean dish, but has many other uses. Try bulgur in mixed-grain salads or with lentils. Millet is a round nutty grain that resembles couscous; it can be used in salads or the stuffing for peppers, or mixed with corn. Oats are not just for breakfast anymore! Breads, cookies, and granola would not be the same without oats. Oats have lots of soluble fiber, which helps reduce the level of "bad" (LDL) cholesterol. Quinoa is another whole grain that's gaining popularity; it's a light, high-protein grain that's very versatile. Add it to muffins and breads or use it as a side dish. Wild rice, one of the best-known grains on this list, isn't really a rice at all, but a long grass. Wild rice complements fish and poultry well.
Herbs	➤ Herbs can give a bland dish a new flavor. Dried herbs stored in the pantry will last for about six months.
Honey	➤ Widely used as a spread for bread and as a sweetener and flavoring agent for baked goods, liquids (such as tea), desserts, and savory dishes such as honey-glazed ham or carrots. The darker the honey, the more intense the flavor. The flavor of a honey depends on the flower visited by the bee. For example, clover honey has a clean, light flavor, and orange blossom honey has a slightly citrusy flavor.
Hot pepper sauce	➤ The intense flavor of hot pepper sauce can turn dull vegetables into an exciting dish. The chiles used are often generic—usually arbol peppers, or whatever is available—and some hot sauces can be plain hot and salty. No matter. There are thousands of hot pepper sauces, and each is worth a try.

Food	Uses

To cut the heat of these hot pepper sauces, take a swig of skim milk, rather than a drink of water or beer. Only dairy protein works to bind the hot substance in peppers! (The hot stuff combines with the casein protein in milk. Cottage cheese and sour cream do not work, unfortunately.) This is another good reason to keep evaporated milk or powdered milk on hand; it will help cool your nerves if you've had too much hot pepper sauce.

Instant coffee, espresso

➤ Instant coffee can be used for making coffee if you don't have freshly ground beans in the house. It adds a bit of tantalizing bitterness, as chocolate does, and a lot of caffeine to whatever you want.

Ketchup

➤ In most homes, ketchup (catsup) is a staple condiment. However, it's also an ingredient in many recipes and sauces. Ketchup is incredibly high in lycopene (and, unfortunately, usually, sugar). Remember to eat it with a little fat first to facilitate absorption of the lycopene and decrease the peak level of sugar in your blood. Look for organic ketchup in the supermarket, with tomatoes or tomato paste (not water, sugar, or corn syrup) as the first ingredient.

Nuts

➤ Almonds, walnuts, pine nuts, pecans, pistachios, Brazil nuts, soy nuts—I love them all. (Peanuts, which are really a legume, can rarely pose a hazard. The cancer-causing toxin called aflatoxin is produced by a mold that sometimes grows on peanuts. This is not much of a problem with modern growing processes; so peanuts are also lovable.) Buy nuts by the half pound and keep them tightly sealed in see-through glass containers. Toasting nuts brings out their flavor and reduces the amount needed in recipes. One of my favorite "fat-first" strategies is to eat just 1/2 ounce of mixed nuts before a meal, as it makes you as much as 4.4 years younger (6 walnuts, 9 cashews, or 12 almonds).

Food	Uses
Oils, healthy	➤ Canola, sesame, and olive oils are mainly monounsaturated fats that help make your RealAge younger. These three oils are sufficient for most baking and cooking purposes (nut, fish, and peanut oils are healthy oils also). Cold-pressed canola oil has lots of omega-3 fatty acids, too. Extra-virgin olive oil works for general cooking and often has a fragrant, distinctive bouquet and flavor.
Olives	➤ Pitted canned black olives are what many of us grew up eating. While they have a place, there are many exciting, delicious multiflavored and textured choices just waiting for you. Look for Kalamata, Niçoise, and spicy green Sicilian olives. All of these olives have clear, distinct, wonderful flavors, sometimes redolent of herbs and spices like cumin, fennel, and bay leaf. All have healthy fat, too. Use them as a relish, on pizza, and in pasta dishes, stews, ragouts, and salads.
Onions	➤ Onions will last for a long time in a dry, dark place in the pantry. You never know when you'll need onions for a sauce, salad, rice dish, or main dish. Use white onions for a clear, clean flavor for Mexican dishes, for grilling, and for caramelizing; use yellow onions for Italian, French, and Spanish dishes; and use red onions for color and crunch. Look for cippolini onions (sweet, small, and flat), Vidalia and Walla Walla onions (sweet and huge), and shallots (sometimes even mild enough to eat out of hand). Onions help keep your arteries and immune system young.
Pasta (whole-grain)	➤ Whole-grain pastas come in a variety of flavors and colors (for example, spinach pasta and jalapeño pepper pasta). Although we recommend whole wheat pasta as a staple because of its fiber content, selecting the right brand is important. Some pastas cook up so tough they're almost inedible. Don't give up! Try different brands until you find one that cooks up just the way you like it.

Food	Uses
Pepper	➤ Pepper is a versatile spice that goes with almost any dish. For the best flavor, whole peppercorns should be kept in the pantry and ground as needed. You can use black, white, and even pink (!), or green peppercorns; look for grinders that can easily grind all four at once.
Potatoes	➤ Sweet, red, and baking or russet potatoes are the varieties you need. Potatoes, like beans and lentils, can take center stage in meals. Also, potatoes are rich in artery-protecting folate. Sweet potatoes are underappreciated, have twice as much folate for their weight as other types of potatoes, and roast beautifully. They also keep well. Look for Garnets, plus the usual Jewels and Beauregards; Garnets have darker skin and lighter flesh, and a sweeter roast. Red potatoes are good for salads because they hold their shape well; look for the smaller "creamers," or small red potatoes of a waxy type. Specialty potatoes, such as Peruvian Blues and Fingerlings, are fun to experiment with and are delicious as well.
Salsa	➤ Salsa has a variety of uses in the kitchen—as a topping for a Southwestern dish or a baked potato, or as a dip for chips. You can also cook with salsa: mix some into egg whites, blend some with an avocado, or pour some into a stew. Use salsa to top grilled fish. Look for salsa that is minimally processed and that is made from whole tomatoes or tomatillos, onions, garlic, and herbs.
Salt	➤ Salt brings out the flavor of foods. I use mainly sea salt and kosher salt. Sea salt is usually ground more finely and, gram for gram, is usually saltier than kosher salt, which has bigger crystals. Both taste richer and fuller, and not as sharp or as slightly bitter as iodized salt. (While too much salt—sodium—can increase blood pressure a little—systolic 1 to 4.7/diastolic 0.5 to 3 mmHg—in most people and a lot in some rare individuals

Food	Uses
	with salt-sensitive high blood pressure, a little salt adds great taste to many dishes. Use it judiciously if your blood pressure is around 115/75.)
Soy sauce	➤ Soy sauce is used commonly in Asian recipes and is a component of marinades. It blends well with other strong flavors—garlic, chiles, ginger, and flavored oils. Flavored soy sauce is available in specialty markets; mushroom soy sauce is my current favorite. Look for low-sodium soy sauce; it often carries much of the flavor of regular soy sauce but not as much salt. Also try shoyu and tamari. Their flavor comes from fermented grains and is often rich and deep.
Spices, dried	➤ Spices are one of the most important ingredients in your RealAge kitchen. When you can, buy them whole, not ground. Here are some spices you should get to know: allspice, bay leaves, caraway seeds, cardamom, cayenne pepper, chili powder, cinnamon, cloves, coriander, cumin, curry powder, dill, epazote, fennel, garam masala (a traditional blend of ground spices), ginger, mace, marjoram, mustard, nutmeg, oregano, paprika, rosemary, saffron, sage, sesame seeds, tarragon, and turmeric.
Sugar (brown, granulated, and powdered)	➤ Although there are four basic varieties of sugar, there are no nutritional differences among them. Common granulated sugar is a fine white sugar that's used for everything from coffee to cake. Brown sugar, colored with molasses, usually flavors candies, condiments, and baked goods. While sugar does not make you younger, a little can add intense flavor. Here's a RealAge kitchen tip: spice muffins (usually flavored with cinnamon, nutmeg, or other spices) made with brown sugar taste less "spicy" than those made with white sugar. Powdered sugar, or confectioners' sugar, is used in frostings and icings,

Food	Uses
	or sprinkled on desserts for eye appeal. Unrefined cane sugar has no more nutrients than the other types of sugar, but does have a more complex taste.
Sun-dried tomatoes	➤ Sun-dried tomatoes have an intense, sweet, slightly salty flavor; they're dense and delicious. You'll find them packed in oil or in cellophane. Stock up in the fall for the winter months ahead.
Tea	➤ Tea, especially green tea, should find its way into your RealAge pantry. Buy it in bags unless you're going to drink a lot. If so, you may want to buy half a pound of loose tea at a time. Green tea contains the most antioxidants. In green tea, the leaves are steamed and dried. In oolong tea, the leaves are steamed, dried, and partially fermented (here, fermented means oxidized). In black tea, the leaves are steamed, dried, and fully fermented. They're all the same leaf, just in different stages. All make your RealAge younger.
Tofu	➤ Tofu can be a great addition to your pantry. Because it accepts flavors readily, tofu can be made to taste like a great many other foods (including chocolate). Tofu is available in three forms: firm, soft, and silken. Firm tofu is solid and dense, and works well in stir-fried dishes and soups, and grilled. It holds its shape well, even after being pressed between blocks, or after freezing, which makes it slightly chewy, and much firmer. Firm tofu is also higher in protein, fat, and calcium than the other two types. Soft tofu is good for recipes that require blended tofu; it's also used in Asian soups. Silken tofu, the softest type, works well in dressings, dips, desserts, smoothies, puddings, guacamole, and cannoli and cream pies.
Tomato paste	➤ Tomato paste is used as the base for a variety of sauces or mixed in with grains. Tubes of tomato paste are especially convenient. Remember to add healthy fat such as olive or canola oil for

Food	Uses

better absorption of the age-reducing lycopene that is found in tomatoes, guava, watermelon, and pink grapefruit.

Tomatoes (canned)

➤ Canned tomatoes come in handy all the time. Use them in sauces, soups, and stews. Whenever you can, buy the organic varieties that are unpeeled (90 percent of the lycopene is within 1 millimeter of the skin). These cooked tomatoes may be even better than fresh, as they release age-reducing lycopene into your system.

Tortillas (corn, flour, and whole wheat)

➤ Tortillas are used in or with chiles, casseroles, soups, refried beans, quesadillas, scrambled eggs, and tostadas. Corn tortillas tend to be the best choice for making your RealAge younger. Even though, traditionally, they consist of just corn, lime, and salt, you'd be amazingly lucky to find them fresh. If they're not fresh, it's easy to rejuvenate them. Roll them up and cover them with two paper towels. After sprinkling them lightly with water, microwave them for 15 to 45 seconds, just until they're soft and steaming. Flour tortillas are often loaded with chemicals and some hydrogenated fats. Colored flour tortillas (those made with spinach or tomatoes) are pretty but no different in flavor or nutrition. Whole wheat tortillas are increasingly available but may have suffered the same fate—added chemicals and hydrogenated fats. Look for those made with oils that are not hydrogenated, and have "whole wheat" as the first ingredient on the label.

Vanilla extract, pure

➤ A bottle of pure vanilla extract is a good substitute for the more expensive, more elusive, incredibly fragrant vanilla bean pods. The seed pods of a plant in the orchid family, vanilla is used commonly in desserts and sauces and also perks up soy milk and cereal in wonderful, fresh ways. Buy a vanilla bean just for the experience: it's long and dark and curled at the end, potent and seeded and just a little gooey in the middle.

Food	Uses
Vinegar	➤ How do you know which of the great variety of flavored vinegars to use? It depends on what you're cooking. Buy one bottle at a time to see what you like and continue until you have tried all of these varieties: balsamic, cider, herb, raspberry, rice, sherry, tarragon flavored, white distilled, and wine (both red and white). Balsamic vinegar is dark and a bit sweet—just a little brings out the best in fruits, grains, and vegetables. Look for traditional balsamic; it's the real stuff. Cider vinegar, which is made by fermenting apple cider, is light and a little sweet. Rinsing diced white onions in cider vinegar takes away their sting of taste. Raspberry vinegar (a favorite) has a fruity flavor and makes salad dressings tangy, dresses up grains, and goes well with tropical fruits. Rice vinegar is a pale, golden liquid that adds, when seasoned, a little salt and a light, lemony flavor. Tarragon-flavored white wine vinegar is nice sprinkled over fish and chicken. White distilled vinegar is an all-purpose vinegar that does well in pickling, but is harsh in cooking except for an occasional chutney. Red wine vinegar goes well with Mediterranean dishes that are tomato-based, and white wine vinegar is gentler still. It can be combined with lighter oils and herbs for a dressing.
Wine	➤ White and red wines are used in our kitchen for poaching, and in soups, stews, and sauces. Avoid wines labeled "cooking wines," as these have added salt, and often their flavor may leave something to be desired. Here's a RealAge kitchen tip regarding wine used in cooking: If you wouldn't drink it, don't cook with it, either. The quality of wine used in cooking really does make a difference.
Worcestershire sauce	➤ Worcestershire sauce is one of the best-kept secrets of good home cooks—just a few drops will perk up meats, gravies, soups, and vegetable juices, or serve as a table condiment. Its ingredients include soy, vinegar, and garlic.

Cooking by the
Seasons

O ne of the great treats of cooking RealAge-smart is to use local produce. Farm-fresh food tastes better than the more traveled variety. So, getting the best to and from your RealAge meals means using local produce. However, local produce varies by the season. Knowing what is harvested in each season can help you choose the freshest ingredients for the healthiest, most fabulous-tasting dishes.

RealAge cooks tailor their meals to what's in season in their area. Foods that are in season are at the peak of flavor, they're the least expensive, and they need the least cooking. Let your garden or a trip to a farmers' market be your inspiration for your meals. Pick the ripest fruit, the crispest vegetables, and the most aromatic herbs; then, let the food speak for itself. To please your eye, mix bright colors. "Food joy" engages all the senses: food should not only look, smell, and taste good but even sound and feel good.

Do you want to cook by the seasons but aren't sure when foods are at their prime? This chart provides this information. While foods are harvested at different times in different regions of the country, the following list shows the usual peak season for fruits and vegetables.

SPRING PRODUCE

Spring is an exciting time for the RealAge seasonal cook because it starts the culinary year. Vegetables push through the earth, nuts and fruits blossom, and the smell of flowers and fresh herbs fills the air. Here's the produce that's in season primarily in the spring.

Vegetable/Fruit	RealAge Age-Reducing Nutrients
Artichokes	➤ calcium, potassium, and fiber
Arugula	➤ potassium, folate, flavonoid, and lutein
Asparagus	➤ potassium and folate
Avocados	➤ monounsaturated fat
Carrots	➤ beta-carotene, potassium, selenium, and some of each of the essential amino acids
English peas	➤ flavonoids and fiber
Fava beans	➤ soluble fiber and potassium
Radishes	➤ selenium and potassium
Rhubarb	➤ fiber
Salad greens	➤ potassium, folate, flavonoids, and lutein
Scallions	➤ organic selenium, potassium, calcium, essential amino acids, and flavonoids
Sorrel	➤ folate and potassium
Spinach	➤ folate, selenium, calcium, and potassium
Strawberries	➤ nutrient-rich and flavonoids
Watercress	➤ vitamin C, calcium, potassium, and magnesium

SUMMER PRODUCE

The warm weather of summer brings new fruits, vegetables, and herbs. The plants that grow well in summer seem to go well together in salads and on a plate. Tomatoes and basil, potatoes and rosemary, corn and beans, and cucumbers and onions are all perfect pairs of flavor.

Vegetable/Fruit	RealAge Age-Reducing Nutrients
Apricots	➤ lycopene
Beets	➤ magnesium and potassium
Berries (blackberries, blueberries, boysenberries, raspberries)	➤ antioxidants
Cherries	➤ antioxidants
Chiles (peppers)	➤ potassium, flavonoids, and fiber
Corn	➤ potassium
Cucumbers	➤ calcium
Eggplants	➤ potassium
Figs	➤ fiber, calcium, and potassium
Garlic	➤ selenium and potassium
Green beans	➤ calcium, folate, and potassium
Herbs (basil, chervil, chives, cilantro, dill, marjoram, mint, oregano, parsley, rosemary, sage, tarragon)	➤ replace salt and unhealthy fats
Kohlrabi	➤ folate, flavonoids, and potassium

Vegetable/Fruit	RealAge Age-Reducing Nutrients
Melons	➤ viatmin A, C, potassium and fiber
Nectarines	➤ potassium and vitamins
Okra	➤ potassium
Onions	➤ flavonoids and selenium
Peaches	➤ potassium and flavonoids
Peppers (green)	➤ vitamin C, flavonoids, and fiber
Plums	➤ potassium and fiber
Potatoes, new	➤ potassium and fiber
Summer squash (zucchini, lita, pattypan squash, crookneck squash)	➤ potassium and fiber
Tomatillos	➤ lycopene, potassium, vitamin C, vitamin K, folate, and flavonoids
Tomatoes	➤ potassium, folate, flavonoids, and vitamin C

FALL PRODUCE

Many fruits and vegetables are at their peak at the beginning of autumn. Juicy apples, sweet peppers, winter squash, and cranberries are some of our favorites.

Vegetable/Fruit	RealAge Age-Reducing Nutrients
Apples	➤ flavonoids and fiber
Beans, shelling	➤ fiber and potassium
Broccoli	➤ flavonoids, vitamin C, calcium, potassium, and lutein
Brussels sprouts	➤ vitamin C, potassium, selenium, and fiber
Cauliflower	➤ vitamin C, folate, and flavonoids
Chestnuts	➤ healthy fat and protein
Cranberries	➤ flavonoids
Fennel	➤ vitamins B_1, B_2, B_3, and C
Mushrooms	➤ potassium and selenium
Pears	➤ flavonoids and fiber
Pecans	➤ healthy fats and proteins
Persimmons	➤ fiber, vitamin C, and potassium
Pomegranates	➤ fiber and potassium
Potatoes, mature	➤ vitamin B_6, C, potassium and fiber
Radicchio (Italian chicory)	➤ folate, flavonoids, and potassium
Sweet peppers, bell peppers	➤ vitamin C, flavonoids, and fiber
Winter squash (acorn squash, butternut squash, Hubbard squash, turbans, pumpkins)	➤ potassium, folate, essential amino acids, and fiber
Sweet potatoes	➤ folate and essential amino acids

WINTER PRODUCE

You might think that nothing can grow in the winter, but some fruits and vegetables reach maturity and their peak of flavor at this time. In fact, some that stay in the ground develop extra sweetness during colder months. Winter's vegetables are appropriate for heartier dishes such as soups, stews, and casseroles.

Vegetable/Fruit	RealAge Age-Reducing Nutrients
Broccoli rabe (rapini)	➤ flavonoids and potassium
Cabbage	➤ flavonoids
Celery	➤ fibert and potassium
Celery root (celeriac)	➤ vitamin B_6 and C
Citrus fruits	➤ potassium and vitamin C
Greens (beet greens, Swiss chard, collards, dandelion greens, kale, mustard greens, purslane, turnip greens)	➤ lutein
Parsnips	➤ fiber, potassium, magnesium, and vitamins B_1, B_2 and C
Rutabagas	➤ vitamin C, calcium, potassium, and magnesium
Turnips	➤ vitamin C, folate, and potassium

RealAge
Recipes

Included in this book are delicious RealAge recipes we know you'll enjoy. Think of them, and of your new, healthy lifestyle, as a giant menu of possibilities: choices for growing younger and staying young. They've been tested for taste and require less than 30 minutes to prepare, start to finish. It's a menu for a lifetime—a long and healthy lifetime—of great-tasting foods.

Each recipe in this book carries with it a RealAge effect. We tell you how much younger or older enjoying this recipe twelve times a year will make you. For example, enjoying Rich and Spicy Black Bean Soup (page 64) twelve times a year will make you 8.1 days younger. Although these calculations are approximations, they clearly provide a direction and magnitude of health effect for each recipe.

Calculating the RealAge Effect of a Recipe

Calculation of the RealAge effect of each recipe is complex in math but straightforward in concept. We already know in detail what each nutrient does to your RealAge. Here's a short summary of a sample calculation of how a recipe affects your RealAge.

We know that consuming 10 tablespoons of tomato sauce a week makes the average 55-year-old man 1.9 years younger. Therefore, if a recipe calls for 3 tablespoons of tomato sauce per serving, each serving provides 30 percent of the weekly benefit. For our purposes in calculating a RealAge benefit, we assume that one serving of the recipe will be consumed twelve times a year. Thus, the 55-year-old man would receive 12/52nds of the benefit derived from 30 percent of the 1.9 year benefit. In addition, for accuracy's sake, we have to adjust the calculations to take into consideration certain mathematical factors—covariance and interactions. Specifically, in our example, the figure of 1.9 years assumes that our man eats an average amount of all the other nutrients that the average American eats. But no one eats this "average" amount. So we assumed, in our calculations, what is known as "the least effect." That is, we have assumed that our man was already eating an ideal diet except for the nutrients in our recipe. This factor is called a covariance factor and is, in our example, 0.25. Combining all of these elements, we compute the RealAge effect of our dish as follows: 12/52 x 0.3 x 1.9 years x 365 days per year x 0.25, or 12 days younger! Because each of the recipes contains many ingredients, the mathematics become complex. Nevertheless, the concept is straightforward.

In addition, each recipe was selected for great taste and ease of preparation. All were tested repeatedly by professionally trained chefs and home cooks alike.

Double Strawberry Blender Blast

4 (1-cup) servings

Preparation time: 8 minutes

103 calories per serving, 4% from fat

3 cups (12 ounces) hulled, halved fresh strawberries

1 cup fat-free or light soy milk

1 cup (6 ounces) strawberry sorbet, such as Häagen-Dazs brand

RealAge effect if eaten 12 times a year:
Strawberries are loaded with vitamin C. I could drink this smoothie all day and skip the vitamin C supplement. Each cup 12 times a year makes you **5.7 days younger.**

RealAge-effect ingredients:
Berries, soy milk (vitamin C, flavonoids, folic acid, antioxidants, potassium)

preparation: Combine strawberries and soy milk in blender container. Cover and blend until fairly smooth. Add sorbet; cover and blend until smooth and thick.

substitutions: Thawed frozen unsweetened strawberries may replace the fresh strawberries; skim milk or 1% milk may replace the soy milk.

tips: Other berries and sorbets will work with this, too: blueberries and lime sorbet, blackberries and chocolate sorbet, and raspberries and lemon sorbet. Experiment and enjoy!

nutritional analysis

Total fat (g) 0.5	Sodium (mg) 18	Vitamin A (RE) 15
Fat calories (kc) 4	Calcium (mg) 70	Beta-carotene (RE) 29
Cholesterol (mg) 3.5	Magnesium (mg) 39	Vitamin C (mg) 64
Saturated fat (g) 0.2	Zinc (mg) 0.9	Vitamin E (mg) 0.2
Polyunsaturated fat (g) 0.2	Selenium (mcg) 12	Thiamin B_1 (mg) 0.2
Monounsaturated fat (g) 0.2	Potassium (mg) 374	Riboflavin B_2 (mg) 0.2
Fiber (g) 5.3	Flavonoids (mg) 2.5	Niacin B_3 (mg) 1.4
Carbohydrates (g) 35.3	Lycopene (mg) 0	Vitamin B_6 (mg) 0.1
Sugar (g) 6.3	Fish (oz) 0	Folic acid (mcg) 41
Protein (g) 5.4	Nuts (oz) 0	Vitamin B_{12} (mcg) 0.04

Orange Fruit Smoothie

4 (8-ounce) servings

Preparation time: 5 minutes

200 calories per serving,
1% from fat

RealAge effect if eaten 12 times a year:
Packed with fiber, this smoothie offers great possibilities and other great phytochemicals. It's been known to make your total cholesterol level fall. This makes you **6.8 days younger!**

RealAge-effect ingredients:
Melon, berries, orange juice, oats (fiber, vitamin A, beta-carotene, folic acid, vitamin C, magnesium, potassium)

preparation: Combine all ingredients in a blender container. Cover; blend until smooth.

substitutions: One glass of orange juice can replace the orange juice concentrate. Frozen blueberries or mixed berries may replace raspberries. If fruit is fresh rather than frozen, add 2 more ice cubes.

tips: This frosty fiber-packed breakfast shake must be served cold. With a few nuts, this works as a great afternoon snack or as a quick breakfast.

2 cups cut-up honeydew melon

2 cups frozen or fresh hulled, halved strawberries

2 cups frozen raspberries or other berries

2 tablespoons frozen orange juice concentrate

4 ice cubes or 1 cup crushed ice

1 large tablespoon quick oats

nutritional analysis

Total fat (g) 0.2	Sodium (mg) 15	Vitamin A (RE) 20
Fat calories (kc) 2	Calcium (mg) 26	Beta-carotene (RE) 120
Cholesterol (mg) 0	Magnesium (mg) 55	Vitamin C (mg) 40
Saturated fat (g) 0.1	Zinc (mg) 0.7	Vitamin E (mg) 0.4
Polyunsaturated fat (g) 0.1	Selenium (mcg) 1	Thiamin B_1 (mg) 0.3
Monounsaturated fat (g) 0.1	Potassium (mg) 600	Riboflavin B_2 (mg) 0.2
Fiber (g) 6	Flavonoids (mg) 0.2	Niacin B_3 (mg) 1
Carbohydrates (g) 28	Lycopene (mg) 0	Vitamin B_6 (mg) 0.4
Sugar (g) 13	Fish (oz) 0	Folic acid (mcg) 51
Protein (g) 4.8	Nuts (oz) 0	Vitamin B_{12} (mcg) 0

Golden Banana Pancakes with Fresh Raspberries

4 servings (12 4-inch pancakes total)

Preparation time: 5 minutes

Cooking time: 10 minutes

315 calories per serving, 20% from fat

**RealAge effect if eaten 12 times a year:
0.7 days younger.**

RealAge-effect ingredients:
Banana, whole grain, fiber, soy milk, egg whites, berries (fiber, calcium, healthy fats, antioxidants, potassium, flavonoids, healthy protein)

1 cup whole wheat pancake mix, such as Aunt Jemima brand

1/3 cup mashed ripe banana

3/4 cup reduced-fat soy milk

2 egg whites, beaten

1 tablespoon canola oil

Butter-flavored cooking oil spray

2/3 cup pure maple syrup

1 1/3 cups fresh raspberries or blackberries or a combination

1 tablespoon thinly sliced mint leaves *(optional)*

preparation: In a large bowl, combine pancake mix, banana, soy milk, egg whites, and oil; mix until large lumps disappear. (Do not overmix or pancakes will be tough.)

Heat a large nonstick griddle or two nonstick skillets over medium heat until hot. Coat with cooking oil spray. Drop pancake batter by scant 1/4 cupfuls onto hot griddle. Turn when pancakes begin to bubble and bottoms are golden brown. Turn and continue to cook until the other side is golden brown, 30 seconds to 1 minute.

Combine syrup and berries. Transfer pancakes to serving plates; top with berry mixture and garnish with mint, if desired.

substitutions: Fat-free or 1% low-fat milk may replace soy milk, and blueberries may replace raspberries or blackberries. The dish will not be quite as pretty, but a sprinkle of fresh ground nutmeg or cinnamon can substitute for the mint; both are wonderful with banana and berries.

tips: Drop a berry or two on the uncooked side of each pancake as it cooks. The heat will gently cook the berries, and the pan will bubble and smear the berries after you flip each pancake. When the warm berries are flooded with syrup, covered with more berries, and sprinkled with mint, you may want to make another batch. Give in and go for it.

nutritional analysis

Total fat (g) 6.9	Sodium (mg) 309	Vitamin A (RE) 22
Fat calories (kc) 62	Calcium (mg) 104	Beta-carotene (RE) 48
Cholesterol (mg) 22.5	Magnesium (mg) 30	Vitamin C (mg) 11
Saturated fat (g) 1.5	Zinc (mg) 0.6	Vitamin E (mg) 0.6
Polyunsaturated fat (g) 1.3	Selenium (mcg) 5	Thiamin B_1 (mg) 0.14
Monounsaturated fat (g) 3.7	Potassium (mg) 300	Riboflavin B_2 (mg) 0.2
Fiber (g) 3.4	Flavonoids (mg) 1.5	Niacin B_3 (mg) 0.8
Carbohydrates (g) 57	Lycopene (mg) 0	Vitamin B_6 (mg) 0.2
Sugar (g) 36	Fish (oz) 0	Folic acid (mcg) 18
Protein (g) 5.9	Nuts (oz) 0	Vitamin B_{12} (mcg) 0.4

Goat Cheese Omelet with Chives and Corn

2 servings

Preparation time: 8 minutes

Cooking time: 5 minutes

RealAge effect if eaten 12 times a year:
Replacing egg yolks with egg whites and replacing fat and cholesterol with protein help you become **0.1 day younger.**

140 calories per serving, 36% from fat

RealAge-effect ingredients:
Corn, egg whites, soy milk (antioxidants, healthy protein, calcium)

Cooking oil spray

preparation: Heat a large nonstick skillet over medium heat until hot. Coat lightly with cooking oil spray and add corn; cook 2–3 minutes or until corn begins to brown, stirring occasionally.

In a medium bowl, beat together egg whites, egg, soy milk, salt, and pepper. Add to skillet and cook for 2 minutes or until eggs begin to set on bottom. Gently lift edges of omelet with a spatula to allow uncooked portion of eggs to flow to edges and set. Continue cooking for 2 minutes or until center is almost set.

Reserve 1 tablespoon cheese and 1 teaspoon chives for garnish. Scatter remaining 3 tablespoons cheese and 1 tablespoon chives over the egg mixture. Using a large spatula, fold one half of omelet over the filling; cook 1 minute or until cheese is melted. Cut in half; transfer to serving dishes and garnish with remaining cheese and chives.

substitutions: Feta cheese or herbed feta cheese may replace goat cheese. Chopped dill or basil may replace chives.

tips: Using a 10-inch, nonstick, sloped-sided skillet makes it easy to fold the cooked omelet in half. For a family of four, double the ingredients and use two skillets.

1/2 cup fresh or thawed frozen corn kernels

3 large egg whites

1 large egg

2 tablespoons nonfat soy milk or skim milk

1/4 teaspoon salt

1/4 teaspoon freshly ground black pepper

4 tablespoons (1 ounce) crumbled goat cheese or herbed goat cheese

1 tablespoon plus 1 teaspoon chopped fresh chives

nutritional analysis

Total fat (g) 5.6	Sodium (mg) 462	Vitamin A (RE) 98
Fat calories (kc) 50.3	Calcium (mg) 107	Beta-carotene (RE) 138
Cholesterol (mg) 119.2	Magnesium (mg) 21	Vitamin C (mg) 3
Saturated fat (g) 2.9	Zinc (mg) 0.9	Vitamin E (mg) 0.29
Polyunsaturated fat (g) 0.4	Selenium (mcg) 19	Thiamin B_1 (mg) 0.08
Monounsaturated fat (g) 1.6	Potassium (mg) 198	Riboflavin B_2 (mg) 0.5
Fiber (g) 0.9	Flavonoids (mg) 0	Niacin B_3 (mg) 0.8
Carbohydrates (g) 10.6	Lycopene (mg) 0	Vitamin B_6 (mg) 0.15
Sugar (g) 1.4	Fish (oz) 0	Folic acid (mcg) 27
Protein (g) 12.2	Nuts (oz) 0	Vitamin B_{12} (mcg) 0.65

French Toast with Spiced Fruit

4 servings

Preparation time: 8 minutes

Cooking time: 12 minutes

335 calories per serving, 6% from fat

2 cups unfiltered apple juice or apple cider

1 cinnamon stick or 1/4 teaspoon cinnamon

1 cup mixed dried fruit bits, such as Sunsweet brand

2 egg whites, beaten until frothy

1/2 cup nonfat vanilla soy milk

1/8 teaspoon nutmeg

Butter-flavored cooking oil spray

8 slices whole wheat or multigrain bread, such as Natural Ovens brand

2 teaspoons confectioners' sugar

RealAge effect if eaten 12 times a year:
The natural goodness of soy protein reduces aging of the coronary arteries (now an FDA-approved claim). This powerful breakfast carries a **RealAge benefit of 8.9 days younger.**

RealAge-effect ingredients:
Apple juice, fruit, egg whites, soy milk, whole grains (fiber, flavonoids, antioxidants, folic acid, potassium, healthy protein)

preparation: Combine juice and cinnamon stick or cinnamon in a small saucepan. Bring to a boil over high heat; boil gently 3 minutes to reduce slightly. Add fruit bits; simmer uncovered 8 minutes or until fruit is tender and sauce thickens. Discard cinnamon stick.

Meanwhile, combine egg whites, soy milk, and nutmeg in a pie plate or shallow dish. Heat a large nonstick griddle or skillet over medium heat. Coat skillet with cooking oil spray. Dip each slice of bread into milk mixture, turning to coat both sides lightly. Cook on hot griddle 2–3 minutes per side or until golden brown. Transfer to four serving plates; top with fruit mixture. Place confectioners' sugar in strainer; shake over French toast to dust lightly with sugar.

substitutions: Diced dried apples or apricots may be substituted for fruit bits. One-half cup liquid egg substitute may replace egg whites.

tips: Reducing the apple cider is an easy way to add extra flavor to this topping. During the simmering time, the water evaporates, leaving a more concentrated flavor behind. Do not soak the bread in the milk mixture too long or the French toast will become soggy. A quick turn of the bread in the milk mixture will suffice.

nutritional analysis

Total fat (g) 2.3	Sodium (mg) 384	Vitamin A (RE) 75
Fat calories (kc) 21	Calcium (mg) 65	Beta-carotene (RE) 450
Cholesterol (mg) 0	Magnesium (mg) 75	Vitamin C (mg) 2
Saturated fat (g) 0.1	Zinc (mg) 1.2	Vitamin E (mg) 0.20
Polyunsaturated fat (g) 0.3	Selenium (mcg) 29	Thiamin B_1 (mg) 0.30
Monounsaturated fat (g) 0.1	Potassium (mg) 597	Riboflavin B_2 (mg) 0.3
Fiber (g) 10.1	Flavonoids (mg) 2	Niacin B_3 (mg) 0.8
Carbohydrates (g) 49.6	Lycopene (mg) 0	Vitamin B_6 (mg) 0.2
Sugar (g) 20.5	Fish (oz) 0	Folic acid (mcg) 32
Protein (g) 9.0	Nuts (oz) 0	Vitamin B_{12} (mcg) 0.04

Sweet Potato Pancakes with Apple and Cinnamon

RealAge effect if eaten 12 times a year:
This recipe makes your **RealAge 5.7 days younger.**

RealAge-effect ingredients:
Sweet potatoes, apple, applesauce, egg whites (flavonoids, potassium, fiber, vitamin C, vitamin B$_6$, healthy protein)

preparation: Shred sweet potato and apple (by hand or in a food processor fitted with the shredding blade); transfer to a medium bowl. Add flour, egg white, egg, salt, and cinnamon; mix well.

Heat a large nonstick griddle or two skillets over medium heat until hot. Coat with cooking oil spray. Drop sweet potato batter by 1/4 cupfuls; press down with back of spatula to form 3-inch patties. Cook 4 minutes per side or until golden brown and cooked through.

Transfer to warmed serving plates; top with applesauce and, if desired, sour cream.

substitutions: One-half cup liquid egg may replace the 1 egg white and 1 whole egg. Ground cloves may replace the cinnamon; use just 1/4 teaspoon, because a little goes a long way.

tips: Use a nested metal 1/4-cup measure to drop the sweet potato into neat rounds. Flattening with the spatula ensures that the pancakes cook through. The cooked pancakes may be kept warm on serving plates in a 200°F oven as they are made.

---

4 servings

Preparation time: 10 minutes

Cooking time: 8 minutes (griddle), 16 minutes (2 skillets)

191 calories per serving, 18.7% from fat

1 large sweet potato (about 12 ounces), scrubbed

1 small Granny Smith apple

1/4 cup all-purpose flour

1 egg white

1 whole egg

1/2 teaspoon salt

1/2 teaspoon cinnamon

Butter-flavored cooking oil spray

1/2 cup chunky applesauce or cinnamon applesauce

1/4 cup fat-free or low-fat sour cream (optional)

---

nutritional analysis

Total fat (g) 4.0	Sodium (mg) 367	Vitamin A (RE) 1881
Fat calories (kc) 35.8	Calcium (mg) 75	Beta-carotene (RE) 11,137
Cholesterol (mg) 53.3	Magnesium (mg) 22	Vitamin C (mg) 23
Saturated fat (g) 2.4	Zinc (mg) 0.5	Vitamin E (mg) 4
Polyunsaturated fat (g) 0.4	Selenium (mcg) 7	Thiamin B$_1$ (mg) 0.1
Monounsaturated fat (g) 0.8	Potassium (mg) 404	Riboflavin B$_2$ (mg) 0.2
Fiber (g) 3.8	Flavonoids (mg) 2.6	Niacin B$_3$ (mg) 1.1
Carbohydrates (g) 35.5	Lycopene (mg) 0	Vitamin B$_6$ (mg) 0.3
Sugar (g) 13.8	Fish (oz) 0	Folic acid (mcg) 29
Protein (g) 4.4	Nuts (oz) 0	Vitamin B$_{12}$ (mcg) 0.1

Toasted Oatmeal with Mango and Walnuts

4 servings

Preparation time: 5 minutes

Cooking time: 15 minutes

475 calories per serving, 33% from fat

3 cups old-fashioned oats, uncooked

1/2 cup coarsely chopped walnuts

4 cups skim milk or fat-free soy milk

1/2 cup diced dried mango

1/4 teaspoon salt

1/8 teaspoon ground nutmeg

1 large ripe fresh mango, diced (2 cups)

RealAge effect if eaten 12 times a year:
Potassium and fiber, plus the linolenic acid in walnuts (an omega-3 fatty acid), make your **RealAge 11.8 days younger.**

RealAge-effect ingredients:
Oats, walnuts, soy milk, mango (fiber, healthy fats, potassium, calcium, magnesium, folic acid)

preparation: Heat oven to 400°F. Spread oats in a single layer on a jelly-roll pan. Place nuts on a small baking sheet. Bake oats and nuts 6–7 minutes or until lightly toasted. Set nuts and oats aside separately.

Combine milk, dried mango, salt, and nutmeg in a medium saucepan; bring just to a simmer over high heat. Reduce heat to low; add toasted oats. Simmer 5–8 minutes or until thickened, stirring only once or twice. Transfer to four serving bowls; top with fresh mango and toasted nuts. Serve with additional milk, if desired.

substitutions: Dried strawberries or golden raisins may replace dried mango; 2 cups sliced strawberries may replace fresh mango. Brazil nuts may replace walnuts. One-half teaspoon cinnamon may replace nutmeg. For a lighter, less aggressive flavor, use true cinnamon, sometimes called Ceylonese cinnamon, if you can find it.

tips: Toasting rolled oats is one way to boost flavor without adding calories or unhealthy fats. Over-stirring the oatmeal changes the texture from smooth to too smooth and a little pasty. Just let the simmering milk do its job.

nutritional analysis

Total fat (g) 17.5	Sodium (mg) 33	Vitamin A (RE) 428
Fat calories (kc) 158	Calcium (mg) 61	Beta-carotene (RE) 447
Cholesterol (mg) 0	Magnesium (mg) 176	Vitamin C (mg) 29
Saturated fat (g) 1.8	Zinc (mg) 3.0	Vitamin E (mg) 2.2
Polyunsaturated fat (g) 9.3	Selenium (mcg) 36	Thiamin B_1 (mg) 0.9
Monounsaturated fat (g) 4.1	Potassium (mg) 793	Riboflavin B_2 (mg) 0.3
Fiber (g) 9.3	Flavonoids (mg) 0	Niacin B_3 (mg) 1.5
Carbohydrates (g) 64.6	Lycopene (mg) 0	Vitamin B_6 (mg) 0.40
Sugar (g) 16.2	Fish (oz) 0	Folic acid (mcg) 48
Protein (g) 20.7	Nuts (oz) 0.6	Vitamin B_{12} (mcg) 0

Pineapple-Banana Frappe

4 (8-ounce) servings

Preparation time: 5 minutes

175 calories per serving, 4% from fat

RealAge effect if eaten 12 times a year:
Chock-full of potassium and loaded with isoflavones, every glassful makes your **RealAge 3 days younger.**

RealAge-effect ingredients:
Bananas, soy milk, pineapple (potassium, isoflavones, antioxidants)

2 large ripe bananas

1 cup low-fat (1%) soy milk

1 can (8 ounces) crushed pineapple in juice, undrained

1 cup pineapple-passion sorbet, such as Select brand (a Safeway brand)

preparation: Peel bananas; break into chunks. Combine all ingredients in blender container. Cover; blend until fairly smooth.

substitutions: Low-fat (1%) milk may replace the soy milk; 1 cup chopped fresh pineapple with its juice may replace the canned pineapple; and lemon sorbet may replace the pineapple-passion sorbet (for extra mouth-puckering tanginess).

tips: This is one time you won't want to use fat-free milk. The light 1% milk gives a soft, roll-around-your-mouth feel that you'll welcome. Add some soy protein powder or silken tofu for extra endurance until lunch.

nutritional analysis

Total fat (g) 0.8	Sodium (mg) 31	Vitamin A (RE) 18
Fat calories (kc) 7	Calcium (mg) 39	Beta-carotene (RE) 41
Cholesterol (mg) 3.5	Magnesium (mg) 40	Vitamin C (mg) 12
Saturated fat (g) 0.5	Zinc (mg) 0.6	Vitamin E (mg) 0.22
Polyunsaturated fat (g) 0.2	Selenium (mcg) 1	Thiamin B_1 (mg) 0.2
Monounsaturated fat (g) 0.1	Potassium (mg) 428	Riboflavin B_2 (mg) 0.1
Fiber (g) 2.1	Flavonoids (mg) 0	Niacin B_3 (mg) 0.6
Carbohydrates (g) 38	Lycopene (mg) 0	Vitamin B_6 (mg) 0.4
Sugar (g) 17.0	Fish (oz) 0	Folic acid (mcg) 18
Protein (g) 3.0	Nuts (oz) 0	Vitamin B_{12} (mcg) 0.04

Mandarin Chicken

4 servings

Preparation time: 20 minutes

184 calories per serving, 28% from fat

1/4 cup rice wine vinegar

2 teaspoons dark sesame oil

1 tablespoon minced garlic

1 1/4 tablespoons julienned pickled ginger

2 tablespoons low-sodium soy sauce

1/2 pound cooked boneless, skinless chicken breast, chopped or julienned

1 1/2 cups drained canned mandarin orange segments

1/2 cup blanched snow peas

1/2 cup drained canned bamboo shoots

1/2 cup drained canned water chestnuts

4 cups shredded lettuce

2 teaspoons toasted sesame seeds

RealAge effect if eaten 12 times a year: 9.7 days younger

RealAge-effect ingredients:
Garlic, oranges, snow peas, bamboo shoots, lettuce, sesame oil, sesame seeds (flavonoids, folic acid, vitamin B_3, selenium, potassium, magnesium, calcium, healthy fat, fiber)

preparation: Mix the vinegar, sesame oil, garlic, ginger, and soy sauce thoroughly. Add chicken and orange segments; marinate for approximately 10 minutes. Add snow peas, bamboo shoots, and water chestnuts. Distribute lettuce on four serving plates. Top with chicken mixture, sprinkle with sesame seeds, and serve.

substitutions: Fresh orange segments may substitute for canned mandarin oranges.

nutritional analysis

Total fat (g) 5.7	Sodium (mg) 485	Vitamin A (RE) 185
Fat calories (kc) 51	Calcium (mg) 107	Beta-carotene (RE) 147
Cholesterol (mg) 49.9	Magnesium (mg) 67	Vitamin C (mg) 77
Saturated fat (g) 1.6	Zinc (mg) 1.5	Vitamin E (mg) 1.0
Polyunsaturated fat (g) 2.2	Selenium (mcg) 57	Thiamin B_1 (mg) 0.3
Monounsaturated fat (g) 2.7	Potassium (mg) 850	Riboflavin B_2 (mg) 0.3
Fiber (g) 4.1	Flavonoids (mg) 2.3	Niacin B_3 (mg) 9.7
Carbohydrates (g) 26.3	Lycopene (mg) 0	Vitamin B_6 (mg) 0.6
Sugar (g) 10	Fish (oz) 0	Folic acid (mcg) 126
Protein (g) 23	Nuts (oz) 0	Vitamin B_{12} (mcg) 0.2

Roasted Pepper and Fresh Mozzarella Panini

4 servings

Preparation time: 10 minutes

252 calories per serving, 26% from fat

RealAge effect if eaten 12 times a year:
Because they stay on the bush a few weeks longer, red bell peppers have much more vitamin C than green peppers. Rich in calcium and beta-carotene, too, this easy lunch makes you **6 days younger.**

RealAge-effect ingredients:
Arugula, bell peppers (calcium, selenium, lycopene, potassium, beta-carotene, vitamin C, folic acid)

1 (8-inch) round tomato bread or focaccia

1/4 cup olive relish, such as American Spoon brand

1 cup packed arugula

preparation: Using a long serrated knife, cut bread into two rounds. Spread olive relish on the cut sides of bread. Layer arugula and basil on bottom half of bread. Cut cheese into thin slices; arrange over basil. Sprinkle pepper over cheese. Drain bell peppers well. Tear into thick strips and arrange over cheese. Close sandwich with top of bread and cut into wedges.

1/4 cup packed sliced basil leaves

4 ounces fresh mozzarella cheese, well drained *(see substitutions)*

1/2 teaspoon freshly ground black pepper

1 to 2 jars (7 ounces each) roasted red bell peppers, as desired

substitutions: The best-quality mozzarella—fresh mozzarella—is always kept in a liquid bath. If unavailable, use the low-moisture form found in most supermarkets. Roasted and peeled fresh bell pepper strips (1 1/2 cups) may replace the bottled peppers; chopped pitted Kalamata or Sicilian olives moistened with a bit of olive oil may replace the olive relish, and baby spinach leaves may replace the arugula, although the sandwich will taste less spicy. Toast the bread in a toaster oven for 2 minutes before slicing it open, just to increase its flavor. Microwaving warms bread but doesn't make it slightly crusty, as toasting does.

nutritional analysis

Total fat (g) 7.2	Sodium (mg) 588	Vitamin A (RE) 128
Fat calories (kc) 64.9	Calcium (mg) 253	Beta-carotene (RE) 228
Cholesterol (mg) 16.0	Magnesium (mg) 47	Vitamin C (mg) 79
Saturated fat (g) 3.01	Zinc (mg) 1.2	Vitamin E (mg) 1.8
Polyunsaturated fat (g) 0.8	Selenium (mcg) 26	Thiamin B_1 (mg) 0.3
Monounsaturated fat (g) 1.9	Potassium (mg) 527	Riboflavin B_2 (mg) 0.4
Fiber (g) 9.5	Flavonoids (mg) 0.1	Niacin B_3 (mg) 2.4
Carbohydrates (g) 65.8	Lycopene (mg) 1.8	Vitamin B_6 (mg) 0.3
Sugar (g) 25.0	Fish (oz) 0	Folic acid (mcg) 43
Protein (g) 13.0	Nuts (oz) 0	Vitamin B_{12} (mcg) 0.2

Grilled Summer Vegetable Sandwiches with Goat Cheese

4 servings

Preparation time: 10 minutes

Cooking time: 10 minutes

245 calories per serving, 33% from fat

1 large yellow summer squash

1 large zucchini squash

1 small eggplant or white eggplant, about 8 ounces

1 large red or orange bell pepper

1 1/2 tablespoons garlic-infused olive oil

1 teaspoon dried thyme leaves

1/4 teaspoon each salt and freshly ground black pepper

8 slices dark rye or pumpernickel bread, such as Baltic Bakery brand

Cooking oil spray

1/4 cup (1 ounce) crumbled goat or feta cheese

2 teaspoons chopped fresh thyme *(optional)*

RealAge effect if eaten 12 times a year:
This dense and satisfying sandwich makes your
RealAge 3.0 days younger.

RealAge-effect ingredients:
Vegetables, garlic, olive oil, dark bread (vitamin C, fiber, potassium, calcium, magnesium, zinc, selenium, vitamin B$_3$, folic acid, healthy fats, antioxidants)

preparation: Trim ends and cut yellow and zucchini squash lengthwise into 1/4-inch-thick slices. Trim ends and cut eggplant lengthwise into four 1/2-inch-thick slices (reserve any remaining eggplant for another use). Cut bell pepper lengthwise into quarters; discard stem and seeds. Combine oil and dried thyme leaves; brush lightly over both sides of vegetables and sprinkle with salt and pepper.

Grill vegetables over medium-hot coals or in a ridged grill pan (in batches) over medium-high heat 4–5 minutes per side or until vegetables are tender. During the last 2 minutes of cooking, coat bread lightly with cooking oil spray and place around outer edges of the grill to toast (or grill in the ridged grill pan after the vegetables cook).

Top four slices of the bread with the vegetables; sprinkle with cheese and, if desired, fresh thyme. Close sandwiches.

substitutions: Extra-virgin olive oil may replace garlic-infused olive oil.

tips: The bell pepper will take longer to grill than the other vegetables. Place over the hottest coals or leave in the grill pan 1–2 minutes longer than the other vegetables.

nutritional analysis

Total fat (g) 9.0	Sodium (mg) 427	Vitamin A (RE) 37
Fat calories (kc) 80.6	Calcium (mg) 92	Beta-carotene (RE) 61
Cholesterol (mg) 6.2	Magnesium (mg) 59	Vitamin C (mg) 22
Saturated fat (g) 1.8	Zinc (mg) 1.1	Vitamin E (mg) 0.9
Polyunsaturated fat (g) 0.6	Selenium (mcg) 29	Thiamin B$_1$ (mg) 0.3
Monounsaturated fat (g) 4.1	Potassium (mg) 464	Riboflavin B$_2$ (mg) 0.4
Fiber (g) 5.3	Flavonoids (mg) 0	Niacin B$_3$ (mg) 2.6
Carbohydrates (g) 35	Lycopene (mg) 0.7	Vitamin B$_6$ (mg) 0.2
Sugar (g) 1.9	Fish (oz) 0	Folic acid (mcg) 19
Protein (g) 7.7	Nuts (oz) 0	Vitamin B$_{12}$ (mcg) 0.1

Roasted Red Pepper and Olive Sicilian Salad

4 servings

Preparation time: 12 minutes

140 calories per serving, 46% from fat

RealAge effect if eaten 12 times a year:
The age-reducing quality of olives, filling your stomach quickly with their monounsaturated fat, is a special feature of this dish. **Its RA benefit is 3.4 days younger.**

RealAge-effect ingredients:
Lettuce, escarole, bell peppers, tomatoes, olives, olive oil (healthy fats, vitamin C, lycopene, folate, fiber, flavonoids)

preparation: In a large bowl, combine lettuce, escarole, bell peppers, tomatoes, olives, and raisins. Combine vinegar and oil; add to lettuce mixture. Toss well and season with salt and pepper to taste. Transfer to four serving plates. Top with cheese, if desired.

substitutions: Dry-cured olives or Niçoise olives may be substituted for the Kalamata olives. Yellow tomatoes are small, pear-shaped tomatoes that have a sweet flavor. If they are not available, substitute cherry tomatoes. One-fourth cup bottled Italian dressing may be substituted for the vinegar and oil. Mesclun (assorted salad greens) may replace escarole.

tips: Bottled roasted red bell peppers make this dish a cinch to put together, but if you prefer a sweeter flavor, use fresh red bell peppers that have been broiled until the skin blackens; peel, seed, and cut them into strips.

3 cups each packed torn romaine lettuce and escarole or curly endive

1 jar (7 ounces) roasted red bell peppers, drained, cut into short, thin strips

1 cup yellow tomatoes

8 pitted Kalamata olives, halved

1/4 cup golden raisins

3 tablespoons white balsamic vinegar

1 1/2 tablespoons extra-virgin olive oil

Salt and freshly ground black pepper, to taste

2 tablespoons crumbled feta or goat cheese *(optional)*

nutritional analysis

Total fat (g) 7.6	Sodium (mg) 322	Vitamin A (RE) 188
Fat calories (kc) 67	Calcium (mg) 81	Beta-carotene (RE) 257
Cholesterol (mg) 6.2	Magnesium (mg) 23	Vitamin C (mg) 64
Saturated fat (g) 2.0	Zinc (mg) 0.5	Vitamin E (mg) 1.53
Polyunsaturated fat (g) 0.7	Selenium (mcg) 10	Thiamin B_1 (mg) 0.13
Monounsaturated fat (g) 4.9	Potassium (mg) 424	Riboflavin B_2 (mg) 0.14
Fiber (g) 2.6	Flavonoids (mg) 2	Niacin B_3 (mg) 1.0
Carbohydrates (g) 14.9	Lycopene (mg) 1	Vitamin B_6 (mg) 0.25
Sugar (g) 8.8	Fish (oz) 0	Folic acid (mcg) 75
Protein (g) 3.1	Nuts (oz) 0.21	Vitamin B_{12} (mcg) 0.12

Tomato Bruschetta

4 servings (16 crostini)

Preparation time: 10 minutes

Cooking time: 8 minutes

210 calories per serving, 25% from fat

RealAge effect if eaten 12 times a year:
2.5 days younger

RealAge-effect ingredients:
Tomatoes, olive oil, garlic (antioxidants, flavonoids, calcium, potassium, lycopene)

1 small whole wheat or French bread baguette (8 ounces)

Olive oil cooking spray

1 tablespoon extra-virgin olive oil

3 large garlic cloves, unpeeled

2 medium tomatoes (about 12 ounces), chopped (about 2 cups)

1 tablespoon chopped fresh basil

1/4 teaspoon salt

1/8 teaspoon freshly ground black pepper

preparation: Heat oven to 450°F. Cut bread crosswise into sixteen 1/2-inch-thick slices. Spray cooking oil spray lightly over each slice and arrange on a baking sheet. Bake 6–8 minutes or until lightly toasted. Cool at room temperature.

Meanwhile, heat a small skillet over medium heat until hot. Add garlic cloves; cook until the skin is slightly charred, about 5 minutes, turning garlic occasionally. Cool, peel, and chop garlic. Use the back of a large knife to mash garlic to a paste. Combine tomatoes, garlic, basil, salt, and pepper. Spoon mixture over toasted bread.

substitutions: You can use canned, drained whole plum tomatoes for a slightly more acidic, cooked flavor. You don't have to roast the garlic, but it makes the flavor more sweet and subtle if you do. Instead of three roasted cloves, one clove of minced fresh garlic is plenty.

tips: For an extra rustic, smoky flavor, grill the bread briefly on both sides on a wood-burning outdoor grill!

nutritional analysis

Total fat (g) 5.9	Sodium (mg) 321	Vitamin A (RE) 53
Fat calories (kc) 53	Calcium (mg) 71	Beta-carotene (RE) 96
Cholesterol (mg) 0	Magnesium (mg) 21	Vitamin C (mg) 17
Saturated fat (g) 0.8	Zinc (mg) 0.5	Vitamin E (mg) 0.8
Polyunsaturated fat (g) 1.1	Selenium (mcg) 17	Thiamin B_1 (mg) 0.3
Monounsaturated fat (g) 3.2	Potassium (mg) 247	Riboflavin B_2 (mg) 0.2
Fiber (g) 2.5	Flavonoids (mg) 2.5	Niacin B_3 (mg) 2.8
Carbohydrates (g) 33	Lycopene (mg) 4.2	Vitamin B_6 (mg) 0.1
Sugar (g) 4.6	Fish (oz) 0	Folic acid (mcg) 34
Protein (g) 6.3	Nuts (oz) 0	Vitamin B_{12} (mcg) 0

Dijon Chicken

4 servings

Preparation time: 10 minutes

Cooking time: 10 minutes

174 calories per serving, 17% from fat

RealAge effect if eaten 12 times a year:
0.5 days younger

RealAge-effect ingredients:
Shallot, wine, chicken (potassium, alcohol, flavonoids, healthy protein)

preparation: Combine 1/4 cup mustard, the wine, Worcestershire sauce, pepper, 1 tablespoon shallot, and 1 tablespoon maple syrup in a shallow dish for a marinade. Add chicken and turn to coat thoroughly; let stand for 5 minutes. Preheat charcoal or gas grill or heat a ridged grill pan. Remove chicken from marinade; discard marinade. Grill or pan-grill chicken 3–5 minutes per side or until chicken is no longer pink in the center.

Meanwhile, in a small bowl, combine the remaining 2 tablespoons maple syrup, 1 tablespoon mustard, and 1 tablespoon shallot. Mix well and serve as a dipping sauce for the chicken.

substitutions: Chicken breasts with the skin on can be used; just take the skin off before serving.

tips: Grade B (the darker) maple syrup adds complexity to the dish; it is a stronger flavor than the lighter, more expensive Grade A.

1/4 cup and 1 tablespoon Dijon mustard

2 tablespoons white wine (such as a Chardonnay or Sauvignon Blanc)

1/4 teaspoon Worcestershire sauce

Black pepper to taste (ground)

2 tablespoons finely minced shallot

3 tablespoons pure maple syrup

4 (4-ounce) boneless, skinless chicken breast halves or fillets, trimmed of all visible fat

nutritional analysis

Total fat (g) 3.2	Sodium (mg) 582	Vitamin A (RE) 32
Fat calories (kc) 29	Calcium (mg) 46	Beta-carotene (RE) 0
Cholesterol (mg) 65.8	Magnesium (mg) 36	Vitamin C (mg) 0.4
Saturated fat (g) 0.2	Zinc (mg) 1.2	Vitamin E (mg) 0.8
Polyunsaturated fat (g) 1.1	Selenium (mcg) 31	Thiamin B_1 (mg) 0.8
Monounsaturated fat (g) 1.2	Potassium (mg) 314	Riboflavin B_2 (mg) 0.1
Fiber (g) 0.2	Flavonoids (mg) 0.09	Niacin B_3 (mg) 15
Carbohydrates (g) 6.9	Lycopene (mg) 0.01	Vitamin B_6 (mg) 0.4
Sugar (g) 4.3	Fish (oz) 0	Folic acid (mcg) 4.1
Protein (g) 35	Nuts (oz) 0	Vitamin B_{12} (mcg) 0.4

Multi-Mushroom Risotto

4 servings

Preparation time: 10 minutes

Cooking time: 25 minutes

502 calories per serving, 14% from fat

RealAge effect if eaten 12 times a year:
Low in fat and very low in sodium, our risotto is bursting with B vitamins, especially niacin. It makes your **RealAge 5.3 days younger.**

RealAge-effect ingredients:
Mushrooms, olive oil, shallots, spinach, walnuts (B vitamins, potassium, flavonoids, healthy fats, calcium)

3 1/2 cups fat-free beef or mushroom broth

1/2 ounce dried porcini mushrooms

1 tablespoon olive oil

1 cup sliced shallots (about 3 large)

2 (4-ounce) packages sliced exotic mushrooms, such as Pennsylvania Farms brand

1 1/2 cups Arborio rice *(see tips)*

Salt and freshly ground black pepper to taste

4 cups packed baby spinach leaves

2 ounces Parmigiano-Reggiano cheese

2 tablespoons chopped fresh thyme or toasted walnuts *(optional)*

preparation: Place broth in a medium saucepan. Use scissors or kitchen shears to cut porcini mushrooms into 1/2-inch pieces; add to broth. Bring to a simmer over high heat. Reduce heat; keep broth at a constant gentle simmer while preparing risotto.

Heat a large, deep skillet over medium-high heat. Add oil and shallots; cook 2 minutes, stirring occasionally. Add mushrooms; cook 4 minutes, stirring occasionally. Add rice; cook and stir 1 minute. Add 1 cup simmering porcini-broth mixture to skillet. Cook, stirring frequently until broth is absorbed. Continue adding broth 1/2 cup at a time, keeping rice mixture at a constant simmer and stirring until broth is absorbed. Repeat process until rice is cooked just through, about 18 minutes total. When all broth mixture is used, stir in salt and pepper to taste and check rice for doneness. If rice is too firm, add 1/2 cup hot water and continue to cook and stir. Mixture should have a creamy texture.

Arrange 1 cup spinach on each of four large plates. Spoon risotto over spinach to wilt. Using a swivel-bladed vegetable peeler or cheese plane, shave cheese over risotto. Sprinkle with thyme or walnuts, or both, if desired.

substitutions: Cremini mushrooms may replace all or part of the exotic mushrooms, and low-salt chicken broth may replace the beef or mushroom broth. Button mushrooms will give you more mushrooms, but not more mushroom flavor.

tips: Arborio rice is an Italian medium-grain rice. To add a subtle wine flavor to the risotto, add 1/2 cup dry vermouth or dry white wine to the sautéed rice and let the rice absorb the wine before adding the broth. The alcohol evaporates quickly, and the whole dish is transformed—just a tinge of lemon-like pucker behind every rich and creamy bite.

nutritional analysis

Total fat (g) 7.4	Sodium (mg) 430	Vitamin A (RE) 154
Fat calories (kc) 67	Calcium (mg) 193	Beta-carotene (RE) 42
Cholesterol (mg) 14.5	Magnesium (mg) 62	Vitamin C (mg) 36
Saturated fat (g) 1.4	Zinc (mg) 2.2	Vitamin E (mg) 3.1
Polyunsaturated fat (g) 1.3	Selenium (mcg) 30	Thiamin B_1 (mg) 0.5
Monounsaturated fat (g) 3.4	Potassium (mg) 683	Riboflavin B_2 (mg) 0.5
Fiber (g) 6.2	Flavonoids (mg) 1.7	Niacin B_3 (mg) 8.2
Carbohydrates (g) 71.2	Lycopene (mg) 0	Vitamin B_6 (mg) 0.3
Sugar (g) 5.2	Fish (oz) 0	Folic acid (mcg) 73
Protein (g) 15.7	Nuts (oz) 0	Vitamin B_{12} (mcg) 0.3

Classic Split Pea Soup

4 servings

Preparation time: 5 minutes

Cooking time: 45 minutes to 2 hours

310 calories per serving, 3% from fat

RealAge effect if eaten 12 times a year:
This makes your **RealAge 7.3 days younger.**

RealAge-effect ingredients:
Onion, carrot, split peas (flavonoids, potassium, calcium, folic acid)

preparation: Finely chop onion and carrot. Combine all ingredients and simmer covered on low heat for 1 hour, or until peas are tender and soup thickens.

substitutions: Yellow curry paste may substitute for the chile-garlic paste or puree.

tips: Simple is sometimes better—if the vegetables are of the highest quality, you'll taste it in this recipe. To add richness (and protein), use chicken stock instead of water, and top with crumbled feta and/or toasted pistachios.

1 medium onion

1 large carrot

2 cups green or yellow split peas

6 1/2 cups water

1 tablespoon chile-garlic paste or puree

Sea salt and freshly ground black pepper to taste

nutritional analysis

Total fat (g) 1.0	Sodium (mg) 20	Vitamin A (RE) 516
Fat calories (kc) 9	Calcium (mg) 49	Beta-carotene (RE) 3083
Cholesterol (mg) 0	Magnesium (mg) 26	Vitamin C (mg) 47
Saturated fat (g) 0	Zinc (mg) 0.4	Vitamin E (mg) 0.3
Polyunsaturated fat (g) 0.1	Selenium (mcg) 2	Thiamin B_1 (mg) 0.1
Monounsaturated fat (g) 0	Potassium (mg) 248	Riboflavin B_2 (mg) 0.1
Fiber (g) 2.9	Flavonoids (mg) 1.7	Niacin B_3 (mg) 0.6
Carbohydrates (g) 9.7	Lycopene (mg) 0	Vitamin B_6 (mg) 0.2
Sugar (g) 3.4	Fish (oz) 0	Folic acid (mcg) 38
Protein (g) 2.5	Nuts (oz) 0	Vitamin B_{12} (mcg) 0

Curried Lentil Soup

4 servings (approximately 6 cups total)

Preparation time: 5 minutes

Cooking time: 25 minutes

285 calories per serving, 14% from fat

RealAge effect if eaten 12 times a year:
A blockbuster for beta-carotene, this winner of a main dish makes your **RealAge 4.6 days younger.**

RealAge-effect ingredients:
Carrots, lentils, onion, red wine, yogurt, cilantro (magnesium, calcium, selenium, potassium, vitamin B$_3$, folic acid, antioxidants, fiber, flavonoids, healthy protein)

1 carton (8 ounces) plain fat-free or low-fat yogurt

2 teaspoons canola oil

1 large white onion, chopped

2 large carrots, thinly sliced

3/4 cup red lentils

2 teaspoons curry powder, preferably Madras curry powder *(see tips)*

4 1/4 cups low-salt chicken or vegetable broth

1 cup fruity red wine such as merlot

3/4 teaspoon salt

1/4 cup chopped cilantro

preparation: Place a strainer over a bowl; line with a double thickness of paper towels. Place yogurt in strainer to drain and thicken while you prepare the soup.

Heat a large saucepan over medium-high heat. Add oil, then onion; cook 5 minutes, stirring occasionally. Stir in carrots, lentils, and curry powder; cook 1 minute. Stir in broth, wine, and salt; cover and bring to a boil over high heat. Reduce heat and simmer uncovered 18–20 minutes or until lentils and vegetables are tender. Ladle into soup bowls; top with thickened yogurt and cilantro.

substitutions: Garam masala may replace curry powder for a richer, rounder flavor. Garam masala is an Indian blend of dry-roasted and ground Indian spices such as curry powder, cloves, coriander, cumin, cinnamon, fennel, mace, nutmeg, black pepper, and dried chiles. Look for it in Middle Eastern or Indian markets and in the gourmet section of some supermarkets. Additional chicken or vegetable broth may replace red wine; it will give a cleaner, more beany taste to the soup. For a spicier soup, add 1/4 teaspoon cayenne pepper along with the salt.

tips: Madras curry powder, representative of curries from southern India, is highly seasoned, pungent, and hot.

Strain the yogurt in the refrigerator the day before to make a tart "cream cheese" you can flavor with minced garlic and Tabasco sauce for a beautiful garnish.

nutritional analysis

Total fat (g) 4.4	Sodium (mg) 633	Vitamin A (RE) 1024
Fat calories (kc) 40	Calcium (mg) 154	Beta-carotene (RE) 6076
Cholesterol (mg) 4.6	Magnesium (mg) 68.6	Vitamin C (mg) 7
Saturated fat (g) 1.4	Zinc (mg) 2.4	Vitamin E (mg) 0.6
Polyunsaturated fat (g) 0.7	Selenium (mcg) 24	Thiamin B$_1$ (mg) 0.3
Monounsaturated fat (g) 2.3	Potassium (mg) 1011	Riboflavin B$_2$ (mg) 0.3
Fiber (g) 7.1	Flavonoids (mg) 2.1	Niacin B$_3$ (mg) 5.2
Carbohydrates (g) 34.7	Lycopene (mg) 0	Vitamin B$_6$ (mg) 0.4
Sugar (g) 8.1	Fish (oz) 0	Folic acid (mcg) 225
Protein (g) 19.2	Nuts (oz) 0	Vitamin B$_{12}$ (mcg) 0.6

Pasta e Fagioli Soup

4 (1 1/2-cup) servings

Preparation time: 8 minutes

Cooking time: 20 minutes

268 calories per serving, 12% from fat

RealAge effect if eaten 12 times a year:
10.0 days younger

RealAge-effect ingredients:
Carrots, tomatoes, peas, beans, olive oil, garlic, whole wheat pasta (fiber, lycopene, calcium, potassium, folic acid, healthy fats)

preparation: Heat a large saucepan over medium heat. Add olive oil and carrots; cook 2 minutes. Stir in garlic and red pepper flakes; cook 1 minute. Add broth and pasta; bring to a boil over high heat. Reduce heat; simmer 10 minutes. Stir in tomatoes and beans; return to a simmer and cook 5 minutes or until pasta is tender. Stir in peas; heat through. Ladle into shallow bowls; top with basil and cheese.

substitutions: Freshly shelled peas may be substituted for frozen peas; stir them into the soup with the tomatoes and beans. Great northern or cannellini beans may replace the kidney or red beans.

tips: Leftover soup will keep up to 3 days in the refrigerator or up to 3 months in the freezer. For extra flavor, drizzle a small amount of rosemary-infused olive oil (Boyajian makes a delicious one) over the soup just before serving.

1 teaspoon olive oil

2 carrots, thinly sliced

4 garlic cloves, minced

1/4 teaspoon crushed red pepper flakes

3 cups low-salt vegetable or chicken broth

1/2 cup (2 ounces) uncooked whole wheat gemelli (small twisted pasta), such as Eden brand, or ditalini (small tube pasta) or small shell pasta

1 can (14 1/2 ounces) seasoned diced tomatoes, undrained (such as Muir Glen brand)

1 can (15 to 16 ounces) kidney beans or red beans, rinsed and drained

1/2 cup frozen baby peas, thawed

1/4 cup chopped fresh basil or flat-leaf parsley

1/4 cup grated Romano or Asiago cheese

nutritional analysis

Total fat (g) 3.5	Sodium (mg) 684	Vitamin A (RE) 11
Fat calories (kc) 32	Calcium (mg) 245	Beta-carotene (RE) 6583
Cholesterol (mg) 27.1	Magnesium (mg) 44	Vitamin C (mg) 29
Saturated fat (g) 0.7	Zinc (mg) 2.1	Vitamin E (mg) 0.8
Polyunsaturated fat (g) 1.0	Selenium (mcg) 12	Thiamin B_1 (mg) 0.3
Monounsaturated fat (g) 2.0	Potassium (mg) 888	Riboflavin B_2 (mg) 0.3
Fiber (g) 8.9	Flavonoids (mg) 2.2	Niacin B_3 (mg) 5
Carbohydrates (g) 40.9	Lycopene (mg) 3.3	Vitamin B_6 (mg) 0.8
Sugar (g) 8.6	Fish (oz) 0	Folic acid (mcg) 55
Protein (g) 19.3	Nuts (oz) 0	Vitamin B_{12} (mcg) 0.4

Glistening Gazpacho

4 servings (about 1 cup each)

Preparation time: 25 minutes

111 calories per serving, 80% from fat

RealAge effect if eaten 12 times a year: 5.2 days younger

RealAge-effect ingredients:
Onion, bell peppers, tomatoes, olive oil, cucumber (potassium, flavonoids, carotenoids, lycopene, folate, healthy fats)

1 cup each diced (1/4-inch) peeled cucumber, red or orange bell pepper, and seeded ripe tomato

1/4 cup finely minced red onion

1 cup tomato juice

3 tablespoons red wine vinegar

3 tablespoons extra-virgin olive oil

2 dashes (or to taste) hot pepper sauce

Salt and freshly ground black pepper, to taste

Chopped fresh parsley or cilantro, diced avocado *(optional)*

preparation: Place all ingredients except garnishes in large bowl and combine. Allow to sit for about 5 minutes. Coarsely puree about half the mixture in a blender or food processor and return it to the bowl. Stir well to combine thoroughly and refrigerate for at least 2 hours and up to 8 hours before serving. Garnish sparingly with parsley, cilantro, or avocado, if desired.

substitutions: Try V8 juice instead of tomato juice.

tips: This soup is very refreshing on a hot summer day. Serve it with a glass of chilled red wine, bowls of olives and nuts, and a side of salad for a quick, nutritious, delicious lunch.

nutritional analysis

Total fat (g) 9.8	Sodium (mg) 220	Vitamin A (RE) 73
Fat calories (kc) 89	Calcium (mg) 16	Beta-carotene (RE) 256
Cholesterol (mg) 0	Magnesium (mg) 20	Vitamin C (mg) 45
Saturated fat (g) 1.4	Zinc (mg) 0.3	Vitamin E (mg) 2.05
Polyunsaturated fat (g) 0.9	Selenium (mcg) 13	Thiamin B_1 (mg) 0.08
Monounsaturated fat (g) 7.2	Potassium (mg) 324	Riboflavin B_2 (mg) 0.05
Fiber (g) 2.0	Flavonoids (oz) 9.8	Niacin B_3 (mg) 0.8
Carbohydrates (g) 8.5	Lycopene (oz) 6.4	Vitamin B_6 (mg) 0.19
Sugar (g) 4.0	Fish (oz) 0	Folic acid (mcg) 29
Protein (g) 1.2	Nuts (oz) 0	Vitamin B_{12} (mcg) 0

Basic Guacamole

4 servings (approximately
1 1/2 cups total)

Preparation time: 15 minutes

178 calories per serving,
69% from fat

**RealAge effect if eaten 12 times a year:
7.4 days younger**

RealAge-effect ingredients:
Avocados, tomatoes, garlic, onion, lemon juice,
chile pepper (lycopene, flavonoids, potassium, folate,
vitamin B_3, vitamin C, healthy fats)

2 ripe medium avocados,
Hass preferred

1 large plum tomato, diced
(1/2 cup)

1 tablespoon minced white
or yellow onion

1 tablespoon lime or
lemon juice

2 teaspoons minced,
seeded serrano or
jalapeño chile

1 small garlic clove, minced

1/2 teaspoon salt

preparation: Peel and seed avocados. Scoop avocado
flesh into a medium bowl; coarsely mash with a fork.
Add remaining ingredients; mix well. Serve immediately
with fresh vegetable dippers, baked tortilla chips, or fresh
corn tortillas.

substitutions: If you use white onion, serrano, and lime
(instead of yellow onion, jalapeño, and lemon), you'll get
a punchier, more robust dip.

tips: If you're not going to eat this right away, squeeze
the lemon or lime over the top of the guacamole rather
than mixing it in. This keeps the guacamole from oxidiz-
ing and browning. If you do have to refrigerate the
guacamole, put a sheet of plastic wrap directly on the
surface, for the same reason. Stir well before serving.
A few sprigs of cilantro, bunched together like a small
bouquet and placed right in the middle, is a nice garnish.

nutritional analysis

Total fat (g) 13.6	Sodium (mg) 10	Vitamin A (RE) 107
Fat calories (kc) 122	Calcium (mg) 20	Beta-carotene (RE) 599
Cholesterol (mg) 0	Magnesium (mg) 55	Vitamin C (mg) 22
Saturated fat (g) 2.7	Zinc (mg) 0.7	Vitamin E (mg) 1.7
Polyunsaturated fat (g) 2.3	Selenium (mcg) 0	Thiamin B_1 (mg) 0.18
Monounsaturated fat (g) 7.4	Potassium (mg) 805	Riboflavin B_2 (mg) 0.2
Fiber (g) 4.5	Flavonoids (mg) 0.7	Niacin B_3 (mg) 3
Carbohydrates (g) 15.5	Lycopene (mg) 1.0	Vitamin B_6 (mg) 0.5
Sugar (g) 2.1	Fish (oz) 0	Folic acid (mcg) 85
Protein (g) 2.7	Nuts (oz) 0	Vitamin B_{12} (mcg) 0

Rich and Spicy Black Bean Soup

4 servings

Preparation time: 10 minutes

Cooking time: 21 minutes

186 calories per serving, 9% from fat

1 teaspoon canola oil

1 small red or yellow onion, chopped

3 garlic cloves, minced

1 teaspoon each ground coriander and ground cumin

1 3/4 cups low-salt chicken broth

1 can (14 1/2 ounces) diced tomatoes, undrained

2 cans (15 or 16 ounces each) black beans, rinsed and drained

1/3 cup chipotle chile salsa or cooking sauce, preferably Frontera Foods brand

1/4 cup chopped cilantro

Optional garnishes: low-fat sour cream, crushed baked tortilla chips

RealAge effect if eaten 12 times a year:
Loaded with the antioxidant lycopene, and not weighed down at all with fat, this deep, dark bowl of rustic goodness makes you **8.1 days younger.**

RealAge-effect ingredients:
Onion, garlic, tomatoes, salsa, beans, cilantro (fiber, healthy protein, calcium, magnesium, zinc, selenium, potassium, vitamin B_3, folic acid, lycopene, antioxidants, healthy fats, flavonoids)

preparation: Heat a large saucepan over medium heat. Add oil, then onion. Cook 5 minutes, stirring occasionally. Add garlic, coriander, and cumin; cook 1 minute.

Add broth and tomatoes; bring to a boil over high heat. Stir in beans and salsa. Reduce heat; simmer uncovered 15 minutes, stirring occasionally. Remove from heat; stir in cilantro. Ladle into bowls; garnish as desired.

substitutions: Canned diced tomatoes with green chiles such as Muir Glen brand may be substituted for diced tomatoes, and vegetable broth may replace chicken broth. Crunchy banana chips, if they're dried and not deep-fried, can easily replace tortilla chips.

tips: This treat can be enjoyed year-round. To quickly separate a head of garlic into cloves, press it firmly with the heel of your hand or smash it with the bottom of a heavy pot. Each head contains approximately 12 cloves of garlic. To loosen the papery skin and quickly peel the garlic, smash the clove with the side of a chef's knife.

nutritional analysis

Total fat (g) 3.0	Sodium (mg) 699	Vitamin A (RE) 69
Fat calories (kc) 27	Calcium (mg) 116	Beta-carotene (RE) 411
Cholesterol (mg) 0.4	Magnesium (mg) 167	Vitamin C (mg) 19
Saturated fat (g) 0.45	Zinc (mg) 2.7	Vitamin E (mg) 0.5
Polyunsaturated fat (g) 1.0	Selenium (mcg) 5	Thiamin B_1 (mg) 0.6
Monounsaturated fat (g) 1.6	Potassium (mg) 1158	Riboflavin B_2 (mg) 0.2
Fiber (g) 10.2	Flavonoids (mg) 2.9	Niacin B_3 (mg) 3.4
Carbohydrates (g) 59.5	Lycopene (mg) 8.9	Vitamin B_6 (mg) 0.3
Sugar (g) 3.4	Fish (oz) 0	Folic acid (mcg) 331
Protein (g) 22.9	Nuts (oz) 0	Vitamin B_{12} (mcg) 0.1

Light but Hearty Hummus Sandwiches

4 servings

Preparation time: 12 minutes

353 calories per serving, 21% from fat

RealAge effect if eaten 12 times a year:
Silken tofu adds calcium and isoflavones; chickpeas add lots of fiber and very little fat. All of these combine to make you **5.2 days younger.**

RealAge-effect ingredients:
Chickpeas, lemon juice, garlic, tofu, salad greens, whole wheat, radishes, olive oil (calcium, isoflavones, potassium, flavonoids, healthy fats)

1 large garlic clove, peeled

1 can (15 or 16 ounces) chickpeas (garbanzo beans), rinsed and drained

2 tablespoons lemon juice

1 tablespoon extra-virgin olive oil

1 teaspoon dark sesame oil

1/2 teaspoon ground cumin

1/4 teaspoon salt

1/2 cup (4 ounces) low-fat silken tofu, such as Mori-Nu brand

3 tablespoons chopped fresh mint

4 whole wheat pita pocket bread loaves (the 6-inch size, not the little ones)

2 cups mesclun (assorted young salad greens)

1/2 cup thinly sliced radishes

preparation: To make hummus: With motor running, drop garlic clove through the tube of a food processor and process until minced. Add chickpeas; process until finely chopped. Add lemon juice, olive oil, sesame oil, cumin, and salt; process 30 seconds. Add tofu; process until smooth. Stir in mint.

Cut each pita in half; open pockets. Stuff pockets with half of salad greens and radishes; top with hummus, then remaining salad greens and radishes.

substitutions: Cilantro may replace the mint, torn romaine lettuce may replace the mesclun, and shredded daikon (a large white radish) may replace the familiar round red radishes. Although cilantro would add that mysterious oomph—a little bit of parsley, a little bit of spice, and little bit of grassy pungency—instead of the sweet brightness of mint, they both work.

tips: Dark or toasted sesame oil, found in the Asian section of the supermarket, replaces the traditional tahini (sesame seed paste) because the oil has a more intense flavor and fewer calories than tahini. Drizzle dark sesame oil over stir-fries or on top of veggie burgers. You'll get just enough hint of its perfume to underline the flavor of your food.

nutritional analysis

Total fat (g) 8.6	Sodium (mg) 526	Vitamin A (RE) 43
Fat calories (kc) 78	Calcium (mg) 257	Beta-carotene (RE) 67
Cholesterol (mg) 0	Magnesium (mg) 58	Vitamin C (mg) 14
Saturated fat (g) 1.1	Zinc (mg) 1.0	Vitamin E (mg) 3.8
Polyunsaturated fat (g) 2.6	Selenium (mcg) 14	Thiamin B_1 (mg) 0.5
Monounsaturated fat (g) 3.7	Potassium (mg) 1093	Riboflavin B_2 (mg) 0.3
Fiber (g) 3.9	Flavonoids (mg) 0.3	Niacin B_3 (mg) 3.5
Carbohydrates (g) 82.4	Lycopene (mg) 0	Vitamin B_6 (mg) 0.12
Sugar (g) 1.6	Fish (oz) 0	Folic acid (mcg) 38
Protein (g) 30.6	Nuts (oz) 0	Vitamin B_{12} (mcg) 0

Ginger, Carrot, and Orange Soup

4 servings

Preparation time: 10 minutes

Cooking time: 30 minutes

83 calories per serving, 26% from fat

RealAge effect if eaten 12 times a year: 8.6 days younger

RealAge-effect ingredients:
Onion, carrots, celery, orange juice, olive oil (flavonoids, folic acid, fiber, calcium, potassium, healthy fat, fiber)

Cooking oil spray

1/2 cup thinly sliced yellow onion

1 rib celery, thinly sliced (1/2 cup)

3/4 pound carrots, very thinly sliced

3 cups low-salt vegetable broth or stock

1 1/2 teaspoons finely grated fresh ginger

1/2 cup orange juice

12 teaspoon salt

2 teaspoons extra-virgin olive oil

preparation: Heat a large saucepan or Dutch oven over medium heat; coat with cooking oil spray. Add onion and celery; cook 5 minutes, stirring occasionally. Add carrots; continue to cook 5 minutes.

Add broth and ginger; bring to a boil. Add orange juice and salt. Reduce heat; cover and simmer until vegetables are very tender, about 20 minutes.

Transfer mixture (in batches, if necessary) to a blender or food processor; blend until smooth. Reheat, if necessary; ladle into shallow bowls. Drizzle oil over soup.

substitutions: White onion will work in this recipe, although the soup will be a little sharper tasting. Sliced leeks (the white part) or sliced shallots can easily substitute for yellow onion.

tips: Slicing the carrots thin allows them to spend less time simmering. Spend a minute to do this, as it will speed cooking. Save a few carrot slices if you would like to add them to the soup once it's finished. They add good texture and make the soup more interesting to eat. Also, you don't have to peel the ginger when you're grating it: it's going into the blender anyway!

nutritional analysis

Total fat (g) 2.5	Sodium (mg) 568	Vitamin A (RE) 2397
Fat calories (kc) 23	Calcium (mg) 43	Beta-carotene (RE) 14,382
Cholesterol (mg) 0.8	Magnesium (mg) 22	Vitamin C (mg) 26
Saturated fat (g) 0.35	Zinc (mg) 0.4	Vitamin E (mg) 0.8
Polyunsaturated fat (g) 0.4	Selenium (mcg) 9	Thiamin B_1 (mg) 0.1
Monounsaturated fat (g) 1.9	Potassium (mg) 573	Riboflavin B_2 (mg) 0.1
Fiber (g) 3.5	Flavonoids (mg) 1.3	Niacin B_3 (mg) 3.5
Carbohydrates (g) 14.9	Lycopene (mg) 0	Vitamin B_6 (mg) 0.2
Sugar (g) 9.4	Fish (oz) 0	Folic acid (mcg) 41
Protein (g) 5.2	Nuts (oz) 0	Vitamin B_{12} (mcg) 0.2

Two-Bean Chili with Avocado and Salsa

4 servings (approximately 7 cups total)

Preparation time: 5 minutes

Cooking time: 30 minutes

332 calories per serving, 31% from fat

RealAge effect if eaten 12 times a year:
What a difference a bean makes! Full of protein and energy, plus the monounsaturated fat of avocado, this dish makes your **RealAge 8.3 days younger.**

RealAge-effect ingredients:
Onion, canola or olive oil, salsa, beans, tomatoes, avocado (fiber, potassium, magnesium, healthy protein, healthy fat, lycopene, flavonoids, beta-carotene, folic acid)

preparation: Heat a large saucepan over medium-high heat. Add oil, then onion and oregano. Cook 3 minutes, stirring occasionally. Add salsa, beans, and tomatoes. Cover; bring to a boil over high heat. Reduce heat; simmer 25 minutes. Ladle into bowls; top with avocado and cilantro.

substitutions: Fresh Italian flat-leaf parsley can be used instead of cilantro for those who prefer the bright, clean mineral flavors of parsley to the perfume and pungency of cilantro. This seasonal recipe uses Fuerte avocados, which seem to peak in fall and winter. If you use Hass avocados, the recipe becomes a spring and summer treat, as Hass peak in spring and summer.

tips: Leftover chili may be covered and refrigerated up to 3 days or frozen up to 3 months. The chili may be drained or cooked uncovered to thicken and used as a burrito filling.

2 teaspoons canola or olive oil

1 large white onion, chopped

2 teaspoons dried oregano leaves, preferably Mexican

1/2 cup salsa, preferably guajillo chile salsa, such as Frontera Foods brand

1 can (15 to 16 ounces) black or kidney beans, rinsed and drained

1 can (15 to 16 ounces) pinto beans, rinsed and drained

2 cans (14 1/2 ounces each) diced tomatoes or diced tomatoes with green chiles, undrained

1 ripe medium avocado, peeled, seeded, and diced *(see substitutions)*

1/4 cup chopped cilantro

nutritional analysis

Total fat (g) 11	Sodium (mg) 757	Vitamin A (RE) 108
Fat calories (kc) 99	Calcium (mg) 61	Beta-carotene (RE) 227
Cholesterol (mg) 0	Magnesium (mg) 92	Vitamin C (mg) 22
Saturated fat (g) 1.6	Zinc (mg) 1.3	Vitamin E (mg) 1.5
Polyunsaturated fat (g) 1.3	Selenium (mcg) 2	Thiamin B_1 (mg) 0.3
Monounsaturated fat (g) 6.6	Potassium (mg) 834	Riboflavin B_2 (mg) 0.1
Fiber (g) 6.0	Flavonoids (mg) 5.8	Niacin B_3 (mg) 2.3
Carbohydrates (g) 32	Lycopene (mg) 15	Vitamin B_6 (mg) 0.3
Sugar (g) 4.1	Fish (oz) 0	Folic acid (mcg) 170
Protein (g) 9.9	Nuts (oz) 0	Vitamin B_{12} (mcg) 0

Roasted Chicken with Pesto and Asparagus

4 servings

Preparation time: 10 minutes

Cooking time: 10 minutes

439 calories per serving, 26% from fat

8 ounces whole-grain pesto gemelli pasta, such as Eden brand

12 ounces boneless, skinless chicken thighs

1 tablespoon olive oil

2 teaspoons dried herbes de Provence or fines herbes

1 bunch (about 14 ounces) asparagus spears, cut into 1-inch pieces

1/2 cup low-salt chicken broth

1/4 cup prepared reduced-fat basil pesto, such as Contadina Buitoni brand

1 teaspoon salt

1/2 teaspoon freshly ground black pepper

Optional toppings: chopped fresh basil or parsley, grated Asiago cheese, and toasted pine nuts

RealAge effect if eaten 12 times a year:
With a generous serving of heart-healthy monounsaturated fats, this dinner will make your **RealAge 2.5 days younger.**

RealAge-effect ingredients:
Whole-grain pasta, asparagus, olive oil, tomatoes (healthy protein, healthy fats, potassium, lycopene)

preparation: Heat broiler. Cook pasta according to package directions. Meanwhile, cut chicken into 1-inch chunks; toss with oil and dried herbs and spread out on a nonstick jelly-roll pan. Broil 5 to 6 inches from heat for 6 minutes. Add asparagus to chicken, stirring to coat lightly with oil. Continue broiling 4 minutes or until chicken is cooked through and asparagus is crisp-tender.

Transfer cooked pasta to a colander to drain. Add broth, pesto, salt, and pepper to pot; mix well. Add pasta and chicken mixture; toss well and transfer to shallow pasta bowls; top with basil, cheese, and pine nuts, if desired.

substitutions: Mediterranean or Greek leaf oregano may replace the herbes de Provence; the flavor will be sharper and a little more aggressive. Pasta that is not flavored can also be used, but I suggest cooking it al dente and using a little more pesto, so the pasta can soak up the flavor.

tips: If you prefer, the chicken may be baked in a 450°F oven for 8 minutes and the asparagus added to cook for another 6–8 minutes or until the chicken is cooked through. Don't be put off by the oil in this dish: three-fourths is monounsaturated fat and healthy for the heart. Tossing the chicken with the dried herbs and then offering a blast of hot dry heat is a nice way to maximize the flavor—just toasty enough to boost it, but not enough to burn it.

nutritional analysis

Total fat (g) 12.5	Sodium (mg) 808	Vitamin A (RE) 102
Fat calories (kc) 112	Calcium (mg) 40	Beta-carotene (RE) 92
Cholesterol (mg) 98.8	Magnesium (mg) 50	Vitamin C (mg) 27
Saturated fat (g) 2.6	Zinc (mg) 3.3	Vitamin E (mg) 2.9
Polyunsaturated fat (g) 2.4	Selenium (mcg) 16	Thiamin B_1 (mg) 0.3
Monounsaturated fat (g) 5.2	Potassium (mg) 554	Riboflavin B_2 (mg) 0.4
Fiber (g) 1.8	Flavonoids (mg) 0	Niacin B_3 (mg) 7.4
Carbohydrates (g) 18.7	Lycopene (mg) 0	Vitamin B_6 (mg) 0.5
Sugar (g) 1.6	Fish (oz) 0	Folic acid (mcg) 109
Protein (g) 29	Nuts (oz) 0	Vitamin B_{12} (mcg) 0.4

Salmon with Spinach and Mustard Sauce

4 servings

Preparation time: 10 minutes

Cooking time: 10 minutes

409 calories per serving, 28% from fat

RealAge effect if eaten 12 times a year:
5.1 days younger

RealAge-effect ingredients:
Salmon, olive oil, lemon juice, spinach, wine (healthy protein, healthy fat, potassium, folate, alcohol, vitamins E, B$_3$, and B$_{12}$, flavonoids)

4 (4- to 5-ounce) skinless salmon fillets

2 tablespoons soy sauce

1 tablespoon each dry white wine, lemon juice, Dijon mustard, and olive oil

1 package (10 ounces) fresh spinach, coarsely chopped

2 teaspoons finely shredded lemon peel *(optional)*

preparation: Rinse salmon in cold water; pat dry with paper towels. Place salmon on a shallow plate; top with soy sauce, turning to coat. Let stand 10 minutes.

Combine wine, lemon juice, mustard, and oil; set aside. Heat a large nonstick skillet over medium-high heat until hot. Add salmon; cook 3 minutes. Turn salmon gently; pour mustard mixture evenly over salmon. Immediately reduce heat to low; continue cooking until salmon is firm to the touch, 1–2 minutes. With a slotted spatula, transfer salmon to four serving plates; keep warm. Pour any mustard sauce from plates back into skillet. Increase heat to high. Add spinach to skillet (in two batches, if necessary); cook until wilted, turning spinach with tongs (about 1 minute). Spoon spinach and sauce over salmon. Garnish with lemon peel if desired.

substitutions: Any dry white wine will work here, as will reduced-sodium soy sauce.

tips: When you buy a salmon fillet, ask your grocer to skin it. To skin it yourself, slide a knife between the skin and the fillet. Although this takes some practice, you will be removing the fishiness of the salmon when you remove the skin.

nutritional analysis

Total fat (g) 12.4	Sodium (mg) 667	Vitamin A (RE) 501
Fat calories (kc) 112	Calcium (mg) 175	Beta-carotene (RE) 286
Cholesterol (mg) 82	Magnesium (mg) 105	Vitamin C (mg) 27
Saturated fat (g) 1.9	Zinc (mg) 1.5	Vitamin E (mg) 4.5
Polyunsaturated fat (g) 4.0	Selenium (mcg) 1	Thiamin B$_1$ (mg) 0.2
Monounsaturated fat (g) 6.3	Potassium (mg) 538	Riboflavin B$_2$ (mg) 0.4
Fiber (g) 3.2	Flavonoids (mg) 0.7	Niacin B$_3$ (mg) 5.9
Carbohydrates (g) 24.2	Lycopene (mg) 0	Vitamin B$_6$ (mg) 0.3
Sugar (g) 0.2	Fish (oz) 4.5	Folic acid (mcg) 155
Protein (g) 22.7	Nuts (oz) 0	Vitamin B$_{12}$ (mcg) 3.8

4 servings

Preparation time: 20 minutes

Cooking time: 10 minutes

314 calories per serving, 20% from fat

3 tablespoons high-quality, aged balsamic vinegar

1 1/2 tablespoons extra-virgin olive oil

2 teaspoons chopped fresh rosemary, crushed

1/2 teaspoon salt

1/2 teaspoon freshly ground black pepper

4 (4-ounce) fresh tuna steaks (ahi preferable) cut 1/2-inch thick

4 plum tomatoes, halved lengthwise

4 slices (1/4-inch-thick) red or sweet onion

1 can (15 or 16 ounces) great northern beans, rinsed and drained

1 cup packed arugula leaves

Tuscan Tuna with Grilled Tomato, Onion, and White Bean Salad

RealAge effect if eaten 12 times a year:
It makes your **RealAge 11.4 days younger.**

RealAge-effect ingredients:
Tuna, tomatoes, onion, beans, arugula, olive oil (healthy protein, healthy fats, lycopene, fiber, potassium, B vitamins, flavonoids)

preparation: Prepare a charcoal or gas grill *(see tips)*. In a small bowl, combine vinegar, oil, rosemary, salt, and pepper; mix well. Set aside 2 tablespoons mixture. Brush remaining mixture over both sides of tuna, tomatoes, and onion slices.

Grill the tomatoes and onion slices 4 minutes per side or until tender. Grill the tuna 2–3 minutes per side for medium-rare. Do not overcook or tuna will become tough.

In a large bowl, combine beans and arugula. Cut the grilled tomatoes into chunks and separate the onions into rings; add to the bean mixture. Add reserved 2 tablespoons vinegar mixture; toss well. Arrange on four serving plates. Top with tuna; sprinkle with additional freshly ground black pepper, if desired.

substitutions: Three-quarter teaspoon dried rosemary may replace fresh rosemary; cannellini beans may replace great northerns; and baby spinach may replace arugula, with a less peppery flavor.

tips: A ridged grill pan may be used if a charcoal or gas grill is not available. Heat the pan over medium heat until hot. Cook the tomatoes and onions first, then the tuna. The rosemary scents the tuna just enough to give it a sharp, citrusy zing. To get extra flavor from the herb, crush it between your fingers before adding it to the marinade.

nutritional analysis

Total fat (g) 7.2	Sodium (mg) 347	Vitamin A (RE) 1296
Fat calories (kc) 64	Calcium (mg) 125	Beta-carotene (RE) 2475
Cholesterol (mg) 56	Magnesium (mg) 161	Vitamin C (mg) 112
Saturated fat (g) 1.2	Zinc (mg) 2.3	Vitamin E (mg) 3.0
Polyunsaturated fat (g) 2.2	Selenium (mcg) 130	Thiamin B_1 (mg) 0.6
Monounsaturated fat (g) 3.8	Potassium (mg) 1466	Riboflavin B_2 (mg) 0.5
Fiber (g) 8.8	Flavonoids (mg) 2.4	Niacin B_3 (mg) 13.8
Carbohydrates (g) 46.6	Lycopene (mg) 3.1	Vitamin B_6 (mg) 1.4
Sugar (g) 16.1	Fish (oz) 4	Folic acid (mcg) 138
Protein (g) 44.7	Nuts (oz) 0	Vitamin B_{12} (mcg) 12

Ratatouille Pasta

4 servings

Preparation time: 10 minutes

Cooking time: 20 minutes

394 calories per serving, 9% from fat

RealAge effect if eaten 12 times a year:
Age-reducing fiber, generous amounts of garlic, and lycopene-packed tomatoes make your **RealAge 7.8 days younger.**

RealAge-effect ingredients:
Whole-grain pasta, eggplant, olive oil, onion, bell pepper, tomatoes, garlic, salad greens (lycopene, flavonoids, calcium, magnesium, potassium, fiber, folic acid, vitamin C, vitamin B_3)

12 ounces whole wheat spaghetti

1 dried ancho or pasilla chile

3 cups diced (1/2-inch cubes) unpeeled eggplant (8 ounces)

2 teaspoons olive oil

1 medium red onion, coarsely chopped

1 yellow or red bell pepper, coarsely chopped

6 garlic cloves, sliced

2 cans (14 1/2 ounces each) stewed tomatoes, undrained, coarsely chopped

1 cup packed mesclun (mixed baby salad greens)

1 tablespoon chopped fresh thyme or lemon thyme

preparation: Cook pasta according to package directions. Meanwhile, heat a large, deep skillet over medium-high heat until hot. Add the chile; cook, turning until fragrant and toasted, about 1 minute. When the chile is cool enough to handle, discard its stem and set the seeds aside for a garnish. Chop the chile.

Add eggplant to hot skillet; cook until browned, about 4 minutes, stirring frequently. Add oil, then chopped onion, bell pepper, and garlic; cook 3 minutes, stirring occasionally. Add tomatoes and chile. Reduce heat; simmer uncovered 10 minutes or until vegetables are tender and sauce thickens. Remove from heat; stir in salad greens. Salt to taste. Drain pasta; transfer to four serving plates. Top with sauce. Garnish with reserved chile seeds and thyme.

substitutions: One-fourth teaspoon crushed red pepper flakes or 1 teaspoon ancho chile powder may substitute for the chile. Omit the toasting step and add the flakes or powder along with the tomatoes. Arugula or mizuna may replace mesclun salad greens.

tips: This pasta dish is loosely based on ratatouille, a traditional French side dish from the region of Provence. Dried pasilla chile provides a slightly sweet-hot flavor. Look for the chiles in Mexican grocery stores or in the ethnic section of your supermarket. Toasting the chile in a dry skillet before chopping brings out the aroma and flavor.

nutritional analysis

Total fat (g) 4.0	Sodium (mg) 466	Vitamin A (RE) 163
Fat calories (kc) 36	Calcium (mg) 106	Beta-carotene (RE) 816
Cholesterol (mg) 0	Magnesium (mg) 58	Vitamin C (mg) 78
Saturated fat (g) 0.5	Zinc (mg) 1.1	Vitamin E (mg) 1.1
Polyunsaturated fat (g) 0.6	Selenium (mcg) 2	Thiamin B_1 (mg) 0.3
Monounsaturated fat (g) 1.8	Potassium (mg) 823	Riboflavin B_2 (mg) 0.1
Fiber (g) 5.6	Flavonoids (mg) 5.1	Niacin B_3 (mg) 2.5
Carbohydrates (g) 37.6	Lycopene (mg) 7.3	Vitamin B_6 (mg) 0.3
Sugar (g) 8.6	Fish (oz) 0	Folic acid (mcg) 41
Protein (g) 6.4	Nuts (oz) 0	Vitamin B_{12} (mcg) 0

Stir-Fried Sea Scallops and Summer Squash over Minted Couscous

4 servings

Preparation time: 15 minutes

Cooking time: 12 minutes

435 calories per serving, 4% from fat

1/4 cup each light soy sauce and orange marmalade

2 tablespoons rice vinegar or seasoned rice vinegar

16 sea scallops (about 1 pound)

1 cup whole wheat couscous, uncooked

8 pitted dried prunes, coarsely chopped

Cooking oil spray

1 red or yellow bell pepper, seeded, cut into 1-inch chunks

8 ounces baby pattypan squash, sliced

1/4 cup chopped mint leaves

RealAge effect if eaten 12 times a year:
Very low in fat and high in potassium, this dish will make your **RealAge 5.1 days younger.**

RealAge-effect ingredients:
Bell pepper, whole wheat couscous, prunes, squash, mint (healthy protein, calcium, magnesium, zinc, selenium, potassium, vitamin B_3, folic acid, vitamin B_{12}, antioxidants, fiber)

preparation: In a medium bowl, combine soy sauce, marmalade, and vinegar. Transfer 1/4 cup of the mixture to a medium saucepan; set aside. Toss scallops with remaining soy sauce mixture in bowl; let marinate at room temperature 10 minutes while preparing vegetables.

Meanwhile, add 1 3/4 cups water to the soy sauce mixture in saucepan; bring to a simmer. Stir in couscous and prunes. Cover; remove from heat and let stand 5 minutes or until liquid is absorbed.

Heat a large nonstick skillet over medium-high heat until hot. Coat with cooking oil spray. Transfer scallops from marinade to hot skillet; reserve marinade. Cook scallops on one side (don't turn them over) for only 2 minutes or until glazed; transfer scallops and juices from skillet to a bowl or plate; set aside. Recoat skillet with cooking oil spray. Add bell pepper and squash; stir-fry 3 minutes. Add reserved marinade from bowl; cook 1 minute. Add reserved scallops with juices; stir-fry 1–2 minutes or until scallops are opaque and vegetables are crisp-tender.

Stir mint into couscous; transfer to four serving plates. Top with scallop mixture and serve with additional soy sauce, if desired.

nutritional analysis

Total fat (g) 1.9	Sodium (mg) 803	Vitamin A (RE) 274
Fat calories (kc) 16.8	Calcium (mg) 113	Beta carotene (RE) 1478
Cholesterol (mg) 37	Magnesium (mg) 159	Vitamin C (mg) 30
Saturated fat (g) 0.2	Zinc (mg) 2.3	Vitamin E (mg) 0.2
Polyunsaturated fat (g) 0.6	Selenium (mcg) 94	Thiamin B_1 (mg) 0.3
Monounsaturated fat (g) 0.5	Potassium (mg) 1517	Riboflavin B_2 (mg) 0.4
Fiber (g) 16.2	Flavonoids (mg) 0	Niacin B_3 (mg) 6.2
Carbohydrates (g) 71	Lycopene (mg) 0.7	Vitamin B5 (mg) 0.7
Sugar (g) 51.1	Fish (oz) 0	Folic acid (mcg) 54
Protein (g) 30.5	Nuts (oz) 0	Vitamin B_{12} (mcg) 1.7

Golden Saffron-Flavored Paella

4 servings

Preparation time: 5 minutes

Cooking time: 25 minutes

353 calories per serving, 15% from fat

RealAge effect if eaten 12 times a year:
Amazingly quick, this elegant dish still manages to make you **0.6 days younger.**

RealAge-effect ingredients:
Brown rice, garlic, olive oil, tomatoes, peas, parsley, mint (healthy protein, healthy fats, lycopene, potassium, magnesium, calcium, vitamin E, antioxidants)

preparation: Heat a large, deep skillet over medium heat. Add oil, then garlic; sauté 2 minutes. Add rice, broth, saffron, hot pepper sauce, and salt; bring to a boil. Reduce heat; cover and simmer 8 minutes.

Stir in shrimp and mussels. Keep covered, simmering until shrimp are opaque and mussels open, about 9 minutes. Stir in tomatoes and peas; heat thoroughly. Transfer to four warmed serving plates; top with parsley or mint.

substitutions: If fresh littleneck clams are in season, you may substitute them for the mussels, or use 8 ounces of each for a dramatic appearance and extra flavor. Mix in 1/4 teaspoon cayenne pepper to replace the hot pepper sauce. You may substitute 1 teaspoon turmeric for the saffron. The color will be vibrant, but the flavor will not be as intense. Look for small vials of saffron in the spice section of your supermarket or in gourmet food stores. If the saffron you find is ground into a powder, use 1/4 teaspoon.

tips: Unlike wild mussels, farm-raised mussels are free of sand and are usually free of "beards" as well. I've also made this dish with just mussels and no other seafood, and it works wonderfully. Use the mussel shells as scoops for the rice, peas, and tomatoes.

2 teaspoons olive oil

6 garlic cloves, minced

2 cups quick-cooking brown rice, preferably Uncle Ben's brand

2 cups reduced-sodium chicken or vegetable broth

1/2 teaspoon saffron threads, crushed

1/2 teaspoon hot pepper sauce

1/4 teaspoon salt

8 ounces (thawed if frozen) medium or large uncooked shelled and deveined shrimp

1 pound fresh farm-raised mussels, scrubbed *(see tips)*

1 1/2 cups diced drained canned tomatoes

1 cup frozen baby peas, thawed

1/4 cup chopped Italian parsley or mint leaves

nutritional analysis

Total fat (g) 5.8	Sodium (mg) 884	Vitamin A (RE) 162
Fat calories (kc) 52.6	Calcium (mg) 123	Beta-carotene (RE) 467
Cholesterol (mg) 240.4	Magnesium (mg) 94	Vitamin C (mg) 44
Saturated fat (g) 1.1	Zinc (mg) 2.8	Vitamin E (mg) 5.3
Polyunsaturated fat (g) 1.4	Selenium (mcg) 149	Thiamin B_1 (mg) 0.2
Monounsaturated fat (g) 2.5	Potassium (mg) 890	Riboflavin B_2 (mg) 0.2
Fiber (g) 3.2	Flavonoids (mg) 2.1	Niacin B_3 (mg) 8.3
Carbohydrates (g) 33.4	Lycopene (mg) 2.9	Vitamin B_6 (mg) 0.4
Sugar (g) 3.3	Fish (oz) 0	Folic acid (mcg) 45
Protein (g) 40.4	Nuts (oz) 0	Vitamin B_{12} (mcg) 2.7

Teriyaki Tofu with Red Bell Pepper and Shiitake Mushrooms

4 servings

Preparation time: 20 minutes

Cooking time: 12 minutes

514 calories per serving, 26% from fat

3 tablespoons dark sesame oil

2 tablespoons light teriyaki sauce, such as Kikkoman brand

4 garlic cloves, minced

1/2 teaspoon five-spice powder

12 ounces baked teriyaki-flavored tofu, such as Soy Deli brand, cut into 1-inch squares

4 cups each broccoli florets and sliced asparagus spears (2-inch pieces)

2 cups each sliced shiitake mushrooms and diced red bell pepper

1 cup vegetable broth or stock, such as Pacific brand

2 teaspoons Chinese hot chili sauce (optional)

3 cups hot cooked jasmine rice (an aromatic white rice)

RealAge effect if eaten 12 times a year:
High in potassium and unexpectedly rich in folate, this recipe makes your **RealAge 8.9 days younger.**

RealAge-effect ingredients:
Garlic, tofu, broccoli, asparagus, mushrooms, bell peppers (healthy protein, healthy fat, potassium, antioxidants, folic acid)

preparation: In a large bowl, combine 2 tablespoons of the oil, the teriyaki sauce, garlic, and five-spice powder; mix well. Add tofu, tossing to coat.

Heat a Dutch oven over medium-high heat. Add remaining 1 tablespoon oil, then tofu mixture. Stir-fry 1 minute. Add broccoli and asparagus; stir-fry 2 minutes. Add mushrooms and bell pepper; stir-fry 2 minutes. Add broth; stir-fry 2 minutes. Stir in hot chili sauce, if desired. Transfer to four shallow bowls; serve with rice.

substitutions: Sliced bok choy may replace the broccoli, and regular long-grain white rice may replace the jasmine rice (aromatic as it is). Chunks of chicken breast could be substituted for the baked tofu, although the chicken will need to marinate 10 minutes to absorb the teriyaki flavor.

tips: Using a large, heavy-bottomed pot makes it easy to move the vegetables around so they cook evenly. A large, heavy-bottomed wok would work well here, too.

nutritional analysis

Total fat (g) 14.9	Sodium (mg) 1087	Vitamin A (RE) 183
Fat calories (kc) 134	Calcium (mg) 272	Beta-carotene (RE) 927
Cholesterol (mg) 0.3	Magnesium (mg) 152	Vitamin C (mg) 126
Saturated fat (g) 1.7	Zinc (mg) 3.6	Vitamin E (mg) 1.1
Polyunsaturated fat (g) 9.0	Selenium (mcg) 37	Thiamin B_1 (mg) 1.1
Monounsaturated fat (g) 6.2	Potassium (mg) 952	Riboflavin B_2 (mg) 0.5
Fiber (g) 6.1	Flavonoids (mg) 4.4	Niacin B_3 (mg) 9.4
Carbohydrates (g) 127	Lycopene (mg) 0	Vitamin B_6 (mg) 0.7
Sugar (g) 3.4	Fish (oz) 0	Folic acid (mcg) 120
Protein (g) 29.1	Nuts (oz) 0	Vitamin B_{12} (mcg) 0.1

Sesame Salmon with Mango-Avocado Salsa

4 servings

Preparation time: 15 minutes

Cooking time: 6 minutes

319 calories per serving, 38% from fat

RealAge effect if eaten 12 times a year:
With much more omega-3 fatty acid than omega-6, this is the tastiest way we know to get your essential fatty acids and make your **RealAge 4.2 days younger.**

RealAge-effect ingredients:
Salmon, sesame seeds, mango, avocado (healthy fat, healthy protein, potassium, B₁₂, folate)

1/4 cup plus 2 tablespoons hot mango chutney, such as Crosse & Blackwell brand

preparation: Heat broiler. Spread 2 tablespoons chutney over skinless side of fish. Sprinkle 1/2 teaspoon salt and the sesame seeds over fish, patting to coat. Place salmon on rack of broiler pan, skin side down. Broil 4 to 5 inches from heat for 5–6 minutes, or until fish is opaque in the center.

Meanwhile, combine remaining 1/4 cup chutney with vinegar and remaining 1/4 teaspoon salt. Stir in mango, avocado, and cilantro. Serve salsa over fish.

4 (5- to 6-ounce) salmon fillets with skin

3/4 teaspoon salt

1 tablespoon mixed white and black sesame seeds *(see substitutions)*

1 tablespoon seasoned rice wine vinegar

1 cup diced ripe fresh mango

1/2 ripe medium avocado, diced

2 tablespoons chopped cilantro

substitutions: Black sesame seeds can be found at Asian grocery stores or the ethnic section of select supermarkets. If not available, use 1 tablespoon of regular white sesame seeds. A tablespoon of Eden Shake may also be used. This bottled table condiment consists of white and black sesame seeds, seaweed flakes, and seasonings, and can be found at health food stores and some supermarkets. This recipe also works with striped bass fillets.

tips: Chutney and other thick, sweet toppings are great glazes for fish. The fish doesn't need to marinate, because the flavor is baked right on. Try orange marmalade or whole raspberry preserves. Experimenting in the kitchen is a very good thing.

nutritional analysis

Total fat (g) 13.6	Sodium (mg) 580	Vitamin A (RE) 209
Fat calories (kc) 123	Calcium (mg) 157	Beta-carotene (RE) 272
Cholesterol (mg) 100	Magnesium (mg) 76	Vitamin C (mg) 22
Saturated fat (g) 1.1	Zinc (mg) 1.6	Vitamin E (mg) 4.4
Polyunsaturated fat (g) 3.7	Selenium (mcg) 0	Thiamin B₁ (mg) 0.3
Monounsaturated fat (g) 5.4	Potassium (mg) 386	Riboflavin B₂ (mg) 0.4
Fiber (g) 4.0	Flavonoids (mg) 0	Niacin B₃ (mg) 7.2
Carbohydrates (g) 44.4	Lycopene (mg) 0	Vitamin B₆ (mg) 0.3
Sugar (g) 6.2	Fish (oz) 5.5	Folic acid (mcg) 49
Protein (g) 25.7	Nuts (oz) 0	Vitamin B₁₂ (mcg) 5

Caribbean Chicken with Black Beans, Sweet Potato, and Lime

4 servings

Preparation time: 10 minutes

Cooking time: 20 minutes

289 calories per serving, 13% from fat

2 teaspoons canola or olive oil

1 medium white onion, chopped

1 medium sweet potato (8 ounces), unpeeled, diced (1/2-inch chunks)

4 teaspoons Caribbean jerk seasonings, such as McCormick brand

1 cup low-salt chicken broth

2 bay leaves (*optional*)

4 (4-ounce) skinless, boneless chicken breast halves

Cooking oil spray

1 can (15 to 16 ounces) black beans, rinsed and drained

1/4 teaspoon salt

1 lime

Optional condiments: mango chutney, plain yogurt, chopped cilantro

RealAge effect if eaten 12 times a year:
Substituting protein for aging fat and cholesterol helps you become **4.2 days younger.**

RealAge-effect ingredients:
Olive oil, onion, sweet potato, chicken, beans, (healthy fat, protein, carotenoids, fiber, potassium, folate, niacin)

preparation: Heat a large, deep skillet over medium-high heat. Add oil, then onion. Cook 5 minutes, stirring frequently. Stir in sweet potato. Sprinkle 2 teaspoons of the seasonings over vegetables; cook 1 minute. Add broth and, if desired, bay leaves; simmer uncovered 10 minutes.

Meanwhile, sprinkle remaining 2 teaspoons seasonings over chicken; coat chicken with cooking oil spray. Grill over medium coals, broil 4 to 5 inches from heat, or cook in a ridged grill pan over medium heat until chicken is just cooked through, 4–5 minutes per side.

Stir black beans and salt into the sweet potato mixture. Finely shred or zest enough lime peel to measure 1/2 teaspoon; stir into bean mixture. Cut lime into four quarters; set aside. Continue cooking bean mixture 4–5 minutes or until sweet potato is tender. If bay leaves have been used, discard them. Transfer bean mixture to four serving plates; top with chicken and serve with lime wedges. Top chicken with condiments as desired.

substitutions: Blackened seasoning mix may replace the Caribbean jerk seasoning mix; 1/2 teaspoon Old Bay seasoning may replace bay leaves.

tips: Adding black beans at the end of cooking keeps the onion from darkening.

nutritional analysis

Total fat (g) 4.3	Sodium (mg) 836	Vitamin A (RE) 1269
Fat calories (kc) 39	Calcium (mg) 75	Beta-carotene (RE) 7424
Cholesterol (mg) 96	Magnesium (mg) 124	Vitamin C (mg) 21
Saturated fat (g) 0.4	Zinc (mg) 2.7	Vitamin E (mg) 3.4
Polyunsaturated fat (g) 1.3	Selenium (mcg) 34	Thiamin B_1 (mg) 0.4
Monounsaturated fat (g) 2.6	Potassium (mg) 978	Riboflavin B_2 (mg) 0.3
Fiber (g) 6.8	Flavonoids (mg) 1.0	Niacin B_3 (mg) 16
Carbohydrates (g) 44	Lycopene (mg) 0	Vitamin B_6 (mg) 0.88
Sugar (g) 7.2	Fish (oz) 0	Folic acid (mcg) 188
Protein (g) 46	Nuts (oz) 0	Vitamin B_{12} (mcg) 0.4

Mushroom Pilaf with Pine Nuts and Arugula

4 servings

Preparation time: 5 minutes

Cooking time: 15 minutes

251 calories per serving, 21.5% from fat

RealAge effect if eaten 12 times a year:
High in fiber and low in fat, this choice makes a terrific dinner: It makes your **RealAge 4.2 days younger.**

RealAge-effect ingredients:
Mushrooms, barley, arugula, nuts (fiber, healthy fat, potassium, vitamin B$_3$, folic acid)

1/2 cup balsamic vinegar

4 large portobello mushrooms (about 1 pound)

Garlic-flavored cooking oil spray

1/2 teaspoon freshly ground black pepper

3/4 teaspoon salt

1 cup quick-cooking barley, such as Mother's brand

2 cups low-salt chicken or mushroom broth

3 cups packed arugula leaves

1/4 cup pine nuts, toasted

preparation: Place vinegar in a small nonreactive saucepan; bring to a boil over high heat. Boil gently uncovered until reduced to 1/4 cup, 3 to 4 minutes.

Meanwhile, remove stems from mushrooms; chop stems and set aside. Coat mushroom caps with cooking oil spray; sprinkle with the pepper and 1/2 teaspoon of the salt. Grill over medium coals or broil 4 to 5 inches from heat source for 4–5 minutes per side or until tender.

Heat a medium saucepan over medium-high heat. Coat with cooking oil spray; add chopped mushroom stems and stir-fry 1 minute. Add barley; stir-fry 1 minute. Add broth and remaining 1/4 teaspoon salt; bring to a boil. Reduce heat; cover and simmer 10–12 minutes or until liquid is absorbed. Stir in 2 cups of the arugula until wilted (about 30 seconds). Transfer mixture to serving plates.

Arrange grilled mushrooms over barley mixture; top with remaining 1 cup arugula and the pine nuts. Drizzle reduced vinegar over all.

substitutions: Toasted chopped Brazil nuts may replace pine nuts, and baby spinach leaves may replace arugula.

tips: Chopping and then cooking the mushroom stems adds flavor to the grain. Make sure you include the stems, except for the very tough end, which you can save for stock or compost.

nutritional analysis

Total fat (g) 6	Sodium (mg) 405	Vitamin A (RE) 80
Fat calories (kc) 54	Calcium (mg) 50	Beta-carotene (RE) 120
Cholesterol (mg) 0.5	Magnesium (mg) 55	Vitamin C (mg) 7
Saturated fat (g) 0.9	Zinc (mg) 2.3	Vitamin E (mg) 0.9
Polyunsaturated fat (g) 1.3	Selenium (mcg) 106	Thiamin B$_1$ (mg) 0.3
Monounsaturated fat (g) 3.2	Potassium (mg) 833	Riboflavin B$_2$ (mg) 0.7
Fiber (g) 9.9	Flavonoids (mg) 0.2	Niacin B$_3$ (mg) 9.0
Carbohydrates (g) 43.9	Lycopene (mg) 0	Vitamin B$_6$ (mg) 0.3
Sugar (g) 2.7	Fish (oz) 0	Folic acid (mcg) 104
Protein (g) 9.2	Nuts (oz) 0.5	Vitamin B$_{12}$ (mcg) 0.1

Poached Salmon with Sautéed Kale and Cherry Tomatoes

4 servings

Preparation time: 10 minutes

Cooking time: 20 minutes

255 calories per serving, 35% from fat

1 cup each dry white wine and water

2 tablespoons lemon juice

1 1/2 teaspoons each crushed dried rosemary and dried dill

4 (4- to 5-ounce) skinless salmon fillets

2 teaspoons olive oil

6 small shallots, sliced (1/2 cup)

1/2 bunch kale (8 ounces), coarse stalks discarded, leaves coarsely chopped

4 small plum tomatoes, quartered

3/4 teaspoon salt

1/4 teaspoon freshly ground black pepper

2 tablespoons chopped fresh dill (optional)

Lemon wedges (optional)

RealAge effect if eaten 12 times a year: 8.2 days young

RealAge-effect ingredients: Salmon, lemon juice, kale, olive oil, shallots, tomatoes, wine (healthy protein, healthy fats, alcohol, potassium, flavonoids, lycopene)

preparation: In a large deep skillet, combine wine, water, lemon juice, rosemary, and dill. Bring to a boil over high heat. Reduce heat; simmer uncovered 10 minutes. Add salmon; poach gently until salmon is opaque and firm to the touch, 3–5 minutes.

Meanwhile, heat a Dutch oven over medium-high heat. Add oil, then shallots. Cook 1 minute, stirring frequently. Reduce heat to medium. Add kale. Cover and cook until kale is wilted, about 3 minutes. Uncover; continue cooking kale, turning with tongs until tender, about 3 minutes. Add tomatoes, salt, and pepper; heat through. Transfer vegetables to serving plates. Using a slotted spatula, drain salmon; place over vegetables. Garnish with fresh dill and lemon wedges, if desired.

substitutions: Salmon steaks, cut through the bone, work well here, too. You can leave the skin on, from start to finish. If you can find it, try Lacinato kale (or dinosaur kale). Stemmed and washed, it has more delicate flavor and texture than most kale. Otherwise, whole-leaf spinach can substitute for kale. Broth can substitute for wine, and your favorite skinned fish can substitute for salmon.

tips: A drizzle of olive oil or horseradish sour cream will add extra moisture to this dish, as will more chopped fresh dill. However, poaching the salmon gently and not excessively is the best way to preserve moisture.

nutritional analysis

Total fat (g) 10	Sodium (mg) 522	Vitamin A (RE) 734
Fat calories (kc) 92	Calcium (mg) 158	Beta-carotene (RE) 1987
Cholesterol (mg) 81.7	Magnesium (mg) 71	Vitamin C (mg) 45
Saturated fat (g) 1.5	Zinc (mg) 1.4	Vitamin E (mg) 7.8
Polyunsaturated fat (g) 5.9	Selenium (mcg) 0	Thiamin B_1 (mg) 0.2
Monounsaturated fat (g) 2.5	Potassium (mg) 504	Riboflavin B_2 (mg) 0.4
Fiber (g) 4.0	Flavonoids (mg) 3.1	Niacin B_3 (mg) 5.9
Carbohydrates (g) 25.8	Lycopene (mg) 3.1	Vitamin B_6 (mg) 0.2
Sugar (g) 3.2	Fish (oz) 4.5	Folic acid (mcg) 33
Protein (g) 19.5	Nuts (oz) 0	Vitamin B_{12} (mcg) 3.4

Seafood Stew

4 servings

Preparation time: 8 minutes

Cooking time: 15 minutes

281 calories per serving,
26% from fat

RealAge effect if eaten 12 times a year:
1.2 days younger. Low-fat, low-calorie, and high in lycopene,
this one's an easy winner.

RealAge-effect ingredients:
Tomatoes, olive oil, garlic, alcohol, onion, halibut (healthy
fats, healthy protein, lycopene, potassium, flavonoids)

1 tablespoon olive oil

1 cup chopped white onion

4 garlic cloves, minced

1/4 cup dry white wine or
vermouth *(optional)*

1 bottle (8 ounces) clam
juice

1 can (14 1/4 ounces)
"pasta-ready" or Italian
seasoned diced tomatoes,
undrained, such as
Contadina Del Monte brand

1 teaspoon each dried basil
and Mexican oregano

1/4 teaspoon crushed red
pepper flakes *(optional)*

8 ounces skinless halibut
fish fillets, cut into 1-inch
chunks

1/2 pound uncooked
peeled and deveined
medium shrimp

preparation: Heat a large, deep skillet over medium-
high heat. Add oil and onion; cook 3 minutes, stirring
occasionally. Add garlic; cook 1 minute, stirring once.
If desired, add wine or vermouth; cook 30 seconds. Add
clam juice, tomatoes, basil, oregano, and, if desired, red
pepper flakes; bring to a simmer. Reduce heat; simmer
uncovered 8 minutes.

Stir in fish and shrimp. Cook until fish and shrimp are
opaque, about 5 minutes. Ladle into shallow bowls.

substitutions: Red snapper or 8 ounces halved sea
scallops may replace the fish fillets.

tips: Although the wine or vermouth (we like vermouth)
is optional, it does add a dimension of flavor—a little
puckery, a little like the sea. Almost all the alcohol disappears with cooking. When time is short, use cans of
"pasta-ready" or "recipe-ready" tomatoes that are already
peeled, seasoned, and diced. They're a perfect shortcut.

nutritional analysis

Total fat (g) 8.1	Sodium (mg) 719	Vitamin A (RE) 121
Fat calories (kc) 73	Calcium (mg) 111	Beta-carotene (RE) 367
Cholesterol (mg) 40.4	Magnesium (mg) 123	Vitamin C (mg) 24
Saturated fat (g) 1.2	Zinc (mg) 2.0	Vitamin E (mg) 1.2
Polyunsaturated fat (g) 1.7	Selenium (mcg) 82	Thiamin B_1 (mg) 0.30
Monounsaturated fat (g) 3.7	Potassium (mg) 923	Riboflavin B_2 (mg) 0.3
Fiber (g) 4.4	Flavonoids (mg) 3.4	Niacin B_3 (mg) 7.6
Carbohydrates (g) 22.7	Lycopene (mg) 3.2	Vitamin B_6 (mg) 0.5
Sugar (g) 7.7	Fish (oz) 2	Folic acid (mcg) 64
Protein (g) 27.5	Nuts (oz) 0	Vitamin B_{12} (mcg) 8.0

Cajun Couscous-Crusted Monkfish

4 servings

Preparation time: 12 minutes

Cooking time: 8 minutes

282 calories per serving, 16% from fat

RealAge effect if eaten 12 times a year: 3.5 days younger

RealAge-effect ingredients:
Whole wheat couscous, egg white, monkfish, tofu (fiber, potassium, magnesium, selenium, healthy protein, healthy fat)

2/3 cup uncooked whole wheat couscous

2 to 3 teaspoons Cajun seasonings, as desired

1 egg white

1 tablespoon skim milk or nonfat soy milk

1 pound skinless monkfish fillet

Cooking oil spray

4 ounces (1/2 cup) extra-firm light silken tofu, such as Mori-Nu brand

1 tablespoon light mayonnaise

2 tablespoons sweet pickle relish

1 teaspoon each seasoned rice vinegar and Dijon mustard

1/2 teaspoon chopped fresh dill

1/4 teaspoon salt

Optional garnishes: lemon wedges, dill sprigs

preparation: Combine couscous and seasonings in a pie plate or shallow dish. In another pie plate, beat egg white until frothy; stir in milk. Cut monkfish crosswise into 3/4-inch medallions. Dip in egg white mixture, turning to coat. Roll in couscous mixture, patting to coat.

Heat a large nonstick skillet over medium heat until hot. Coat heavily with cooking oil spray. Add fish and coat with additional cooking oil spray. Do not crowd pan. Cook fish in batches or use two skillets, if necessary. Cook until fish is opaque and firm to the touch, about 3–4 minutes per side.

Meanwhile, blend tofu and mayonnaise in a food processor or blender until fairly smooth. Stir in pickle relish, vinegar, mustard, dill, and salt. Serve fish with sauce and garnish as desired.

substitutions: Diced sweet or dill pickles may replace pickle relish, and Creole or blackening seasoning mix may replace Cajun seasonings. Monkfish (also known as lotte or anglerfish) is a low-fat fish with a firm texture and mild, sweet flavor. If not available, substitute with Pacific halibut fillets that have been cut crosswise into 3/4-inch-thick slices.

nutritional analysis

Total fat (g) 5.0	Sodium (mg) 163	Vitamin A (RE) 49
Fat calories (kc) 44.6	Calcium (mg) 103	Beta-carotene (RE) 6
Cholesterol (mg) 36.3	Magnesium (mg) 134	Vitamin C (mg) 0.5
Saturated fat (g) 1.2	Zinc (mg) 1.0	Vitamin E (mg) 1.0
Polyunsaturated fat (g) 2.5	Selenium (mcg) 53	Thiamin B_1 (mg) 0.1
Monounsaturated fat (g) 2.1	Potassium (mg) 589	Riboflavin B_2 (mg) 0.2
Fiber (g) 5.2	Flavonoids (mg) 0	Niacin B_3 (mg) 7.2
Carbohydrates (g) 27.5	Lycopene (mg) 0	Vitamin B_6 (mg) 0.4
Sugar (g) 0.3	Fish (oz) 4	Folic acid (mcg) 24
Protein (g) 29.9	Nuts (oz) 0	Vitamin B_{12} (mcg) 1.2

Grilled Sea Bass with Red Lentils and Kale

4 servings

Preparation time: 10 minutes

Cooking time: 20 minutes

294 calories per serving, 12% from fat

RealAge effect if eaten 12 times a year:
The antioxidants in this incredibly delicious dish are too numerous to mention—but let it be said that this dish makes your **RealAge 10.4 days younger.**

RealAge-effect ingredients: Sea bass, garlic, lentils, kale, sesame seeds (antioxidants, healthy protein, healthy fat, fiber, potassium, magnesium, calcium, folate, vitamin E)

1 pound fresh sea bass fillet, cut into four portions about 1/2 inch thick

2 tablespoons soy sauce

1 tablespoon mirin (rice wine)

2 garlic cloves, minced

1 teaspoon finely grated fresh ginger

1 teaspoon dark sesame oil

1 cup red lentils

2 cups low-salt chicken broth

4 cups packed sliced kale (4 ounces)

2 teaspoons sesame seeds, toasted (*optional*)

preparation: Prepare a charcoal or gas grill. Place fish on a shallow plate. Combine soy sauce, mirin, garlic, ginger, and sesame oil; mix well. Pour over fish, turning to coat. Let stand 10 minutes. Meanwhile, combine lentils and broth in a large, deep skillet. Bring to a boil over high heat. Reduce heat; simmer uncovered 10 minutes; stirring occasionally. Add kale; cover and simmer 5 minutes or until lentils and kale are tender, stirring once.

Drain fish, reserving marinade. Grill over medium-high heat 3 to 4 minutes per side or until fish is opaque in center. Transfer marinade to a small saucepan; add 1 tablespoon water. Bring to a boil; boil gently 30 seconds.

Spoon lentil mixture onto four warmed serving plates; top with fish. Sprinkle with sesame seeds, if desired. Drizzle boiled marinade over fish and lentil mixture.

substitutions: Halibut, red snapper, or striped bass may replace the sea bass; tamari may replace soy sauce; dry sherry may replace mirin; vegetable broth may replace chicken broth; and Swiss chard or beet greens may replace kale.

tips: Cook sea bass fillets until they are opaque in the center or firm to the touch. If they are thicker than 1/2 inch, add a minute or two to the grilling time. The fish may also be cooked in a preheated ridged grill pan over medium-high heat.

nutritional analysis

Total fat (g) 4.0	Sodium (mg) 657	Vitamin A (RE) 1035
Fat calories (kc) 36	Calcium (mg) 155	Beta-carotene (RE) 966
Cholesterol (mg) 60.5	Magnesium (mg) 124	Vitamin C (mg) 57
Saturated fat (g) 0.6	Zinc (mg) 1.9	Vitamin E (mg) 12
Polyunsaturated fat (g) 1.8	Selenium (mcg) 18	Thiamin B_1 (mg) 0.4
Monounsaturated fat (g) 1.6	Potassium (mg) 908	Riboflavin B_2 (mg) 0.4
Fiber (g) 8.9	Flavonoids (mg) 0.3	Niacin B_3 (mg) 6.0
Carbohydrates (g) 25	Lycopene (mg) 0	Vitamin B_6 (mg) 0.8
Sugar (g) 4.9	Fish (oz) 4	Folic acid (mcg) 62
Protein (g) 36.7	Nuts (oz) 0	Vitamin B_{12} (mcg) 0.5

Rainbow Moo Shu Shrimp Roll-Ups

4 servings (2 roll-ups per serving)

Preparation time: 20 minutes

Cooking time: 5 minutes

270 calories per serving, 6% from fat

RealAge effect if eaten 12 times a year:
Full of complex carbohydrates, but virtually no sugar, eating this makes your **RealAge 11.8 days younger.**

RealAge-effect ingredients:
Chile puree, bell peppers, coleslaw, onions, whole wheat (fiber, antioxidants, potassium)

12 ounces uncooked peeled and deveined small, medium, or halved large shrimp, thawed if frozen

2 tablespoons chile puree, such as Lee Kum Kee or China Bowl brands

Garlic-flavored cooking oil spray

1 each red and yellow bell pepper, cut into short, thin strips

4 cups coleslaw mix (shredded cabbage and carrots)

8 scallions, cut into 1/2-inch slices

1/4 cup oyster sauce, such as Dynasty or Kame brands

1 tablespoon cornstarch

8 (10-inch) whole wheat or honey whole wheat flour tortillas, such as Tumaro's brand, warmed

2 teaspoons coriander seeds, coarsely crushed (optional)

preparation: In a medium bowl, combine shrimp and chile puree, tossing to coat. Heat a Dutch oven or large saucepan over medium heat; coat with cooking oil spray. Add shrimp; stir-fry 1 minute. Add bell peppers, coleslaw mix, and scallions; stir-fry 1 minute. Add oyster sauce; stir-fry 2 minutes or until shrimp are opaque and vegetables are crisp-tender.

Combine cornstarch with 1 tablespoon cold water; mix well. Stir into shrimp mixture; cook 1 minute or until thickened, stirring constantly. Spoon mixture down center of tortillas; sprinkle coriander seeds over mixture, if desired. Fold one end of tortilla over filling; roll up burrito fashion.

substitutions: Shredded napa cabbage may replace the coleslaw mix, and hoisin sauce may replace the oyster sauce.

tips: Adding the cornstarch slurry at the end of cooking helps to keep the juices inside the vegetables. The touch of crushed coriander seed is worth the extra effort. Just a little gives a bit of spiciness to the dish.

nutritional analysis

Total fat (g) 1.9	Sodium (mg) 968	Vitamin A (RE) 246
Fat calories (kc) 17	Calcium (mg) 195	Beta-carotene (RE) 601
Cholesterol (mg) 183.0	Magnesium (mg) 62	Vitamin C (mg) 83
Saturated fat (g) 0.1	Zinc (mg) 2.8	Vitamin E (mg) 10.1
Polyunsaturated fat (g) 0.8	Selenium (mcg) 65	Thiamin B_1 (mg) 0.17
Monounsaturated fat (g) 0.8	Potassium (mg) 569	Riboflavin B_2 (mg) 0.30
Fiber (g) 7.2	Flavonoids (mg) 1.6	Niacin B_3 (mg) 4.9
Carbohydrates (g) 57.4	Lycopene (mg) 0.7	Vitamin B_6 (mg) 0.4
Sugar (g) 2.1	Fish (oz) 0	Folic acid (mcg) 55
Protein (g) 25.3	Nuts (oz) 0	Vitamin B_{12} (mcg) 1.4

Pistachio Pilaf with Butternut Squash and Cranberry Sauce

4 servings

Preparation time: 8 minutes

Cooking time: 20 minutes

363 calories per serving, 22% from fat

RealAge effect if eaten 12 times a year:
High in potassium, flavonoids, and fiber, this beautifully colored fork-tender dish makes your **RealAge 8.7 days younger.**

RealAge-effect ingredients:
Wheat pilaf, olive oil, squash, cranberry juice, pistachios (healthy protein, calcium, magnesium, zinc, selenium, potassium, vitamin B₃, folic acid, fiber, healthy fats, flavonoids, antioxidants)

1 box (6 ounces) wheat pilaf mix, such as Near East brand

1 tablespoon olive oil

1 large butternut squash, about 2 1/2 pounds

1/2 cup plus 3 tablespoons cranberry chutney, such as Crosse & Blackwell brand

1/4 cup cranberry juice cocktail

2 tablespoons chopped crystallized ginger

1/3 cup coarsely chopped pistachios, toasted

preparation: Prepare pilaf according to package directions using 1 tablespoon olive oil rather than butter. Meanwhile, cut squash in half lengthwise; discard seeds and membrane. Cut squash halves crosswise into quarters, then cut each quarter lengthwise into four wedges, forming 16 pieces of squash. Place squash skin side down in a microwave-safe dish. Brush 3 tablespoons of the chutney over squash flesh. Cover with wax paper; microwave at high power until squash is fork-tender, 12–16 minutes, rotating dish twice if microwave oven does not have a turntable.

Meanwhile, in a small saucepan, combine remaining 1/2 cup chutney, cranberry juice, and ginger. Bring to a simmer over medium heat. Simmer 2–3 minutes or until slightly thickened.

Transfer pilaf to serving plates; top with squash. Spoon sauce over all; top with pistachios.

substitutions: This is a very flexible recipe. Acorn squash may replace butternut squash (both are "winter" varieties), white grape juice may replace cranberry juice cocktail, mango or peach chutney may replace cranberry chutney, and soy nuts may replace pistachios.

nutritional analysis

Total fat (g) 9.0	Sodium (mg) 520	Vitamin A (RE) 797
Fat calories (kc) 81.3	Calcium (mg) 87	Beta-carotene (RE) 4766
Cholesterol (mg) 0	Magnesium (mg) 123	Vitamin C (mg) 28
Saturated fat (g) 1.2	Zinc (mg) 1.2	Vitamin E (mg) 1.2
Polyunsaturated fat (g) 1.3	Selenium (mcg) 2	Thiamin B₁ (mg) 0.3
Monounsaturated fat (g) 5.9	Potassium (mg) 671	Riboflavin B₂ (mg) 0.1
Fiber (g) 13.4	Flavonoids (mg) 10.5	Niacin B₃ (mg) 3.5
Carbohydrates (g) 67.3	Lycopene (mg) 0	Vitamin B₆ (mg) 0.3
Sugar (g) 7.0	Fish (oz) 0	Folic acid (mcg) 48
Protein (g) 8.4	Nuts (oz) 0.4	Vitamin B₁₂ (mcg) 0

Smoked Mozzarella and Veggie-Stuffed Pizza

4 servings

Preparation time: 8 minutes

Cooking time: 14 minutes

297 calories per serving, 29% from fat

Cooking oil spray

1 pound fresh, cut stir-fry vegetables (packaged or from the salad bar), such as broccoli, zucchini, mushrooms, red onion, bell peppers, and julienned carrots

Salt and freshly ground black pepper

1/4 cup tomato paste

2 tablespoons olive relish, such as American Spoon brand

2 tablespoons sun-dried tomato bits, such as Sonoma brand

1 (12-inch or 10-ounce) prepared thin pizza crust, such as Boboli brand

1/4 cup chopped mixed green herbs such as chives, thyme, parsley, and basil

1/2 cup (2 ounces) finely shredded smoked mozzarella cheese

RealAge effect if eaten 12 times a year: One huge slice has less than 300 calories but plenty of lycopene and potassium, making your **RealAge younger by 10.0 days.**

RealAge-effect ingredients:
Vegetables, tomato paste (beta-carotene, potassium, fiber, healthy protein, flavonoids, lycopene)

preparation: Heat oven to 425°F. Heat a large nonstick skillet over medium-high heat until hot. Coat with cooking oil spray; add vegetables. Stir-fry 3–4 minutes or until vegetables are crisp-tender. Salt and pepper to taste.

Combine tomato paste, olive relish, and sun-dried tomato bits. Spread over pizza crust; top with cooked vegetables, herbs, and cheese, in that order. Bake the pizza directly on the oven rack for approximately 10 minutes, or until crust is golden brown and cheese melts.

substitutions: Olive paste, tapenade (olive-caper paste), or olivada (olive paste without capers) may be substituted for the olive relish. Look for jars of this rich Mediterranean mixture in specialty food markets and many supermarkets. If you can't find olive relish, substitute 2 tablespoons of any available commercial mixture of finely diced olives, oil, and other ingredients—perhaps garlic, anchovies, lemon juice, capers, or carrots. Smoked Gouda or Lorraine cheese may replace the smoked mozzarella.

tips: Baking the pizza directly on the oven rack produces a very crisp crust. If you don't have a pizza paddle (a broad, flat wooden board that has a handle), use a large cookie sheet to remove the pizza from the oven. You can more than double the flavor by using dried and canned tomatoes together.

nutritional analysis

Total fat (g) 9.5	Sodium (mg) 682	Vitamin A (RE) 362
Fat calories (kc) 85.5	Calcium (mg) 170	Beta-carotene (RE) 564
Cholesterol (mg) 8.0	Magnesium (mg) 47	Vitamin C (mg) 38
Saturated fat (g) 3.0	Zinc (mg) 1.2	Vitamin E (mg) 0.76
Polyunsaturated fat (g) 1.9	Selenium (mcg) 3	Thiamin B_1 (mg) 0.3
Monounsaturated fat (g) 3.5	Potassium (mg) 481	Riboflavin B_2 (mg) 0.3
Fiber (g) 5.3	Flavonoids (mg) 2.8	Niacin B_3 (mg) 3.3
Carbohydrates (g) 42.7	Lycopene (mg) 4.2	Vitamin B_6 (mg) 0.2
Sugar (g) 3.7	Fish (oz) 0	Folic acid (mcg) 64
Protein (g) 12.2	Nuts (oz) 0	Vitamin B_{12} (mcg) 0.12

Meaty Tofu and Stir-Fried Bok Choy over Udon Noodles

4 servings

Preparation time: 12 minutes

Cooking time: 8 minutes

387 calories per serving, 24% from fat

RealAge effect if eaten 12 times a year:
Stocked with potassium and magnesium, this dish makes your **RealAge 3.0 days younger.**

RealAge-effect ingredients:
Buckwheat noodles, tofu, sesame oil, garlic, bok choy, carrots (magnesium, calcium, potassium, beta-carotene, vitamin C, fiber, healthy protein, healthy fat, folic acid)

8 ounces udon noodles (thick Japanese buckwheat noodles)

2 tablespoons seasoned black bean paste

2 tablespoons mirin (rice wine)

10 ounces firm-style tofu, such as White Wave brand

3 teaspoons dark sesame oil

4 garlic cloves, minced

1 small head or 1/2 large head bok choy, sliced 1/4 inch thick, stems and leaves separated

2 cups julienned carrots (packaged or from the supermarket salad bar)

1/4 cup julienned daikon or red radish (optional)

preparation: Cook noodles according to package directions. Meanwhile, combine black bean paste and mirin; mix well. Press the block of tofu between paper towels to absorb excess moisture. Cut tofu into 3/4-inch slices; cut slices into 1-inch squares. Toss tofu with 2 tablespoons black bean mixture and set aside.

Heat a large, deep nonstick skillet over medium-high heat. Add 1 teaspoon of the oil, the garlic, and the bok choy stems; stir-fry 2 minutes. Add bok choy leaves, carrots, and tofu mixture; stir-fry 2 minutes or until the vegetables are crisp-tender. Salt to taste.

Drain noodles; toss with remaining black bean mixture and remaining 2 teaspoons sesame oil. Transfer to serving plates. Spoon tofu mixture over noodles; if desired, garnish with radish.

substitutions: Hoisin or teriyaki sauce may replace black bean mixture—both will make the dish much sweeter but still tasty. Whole wheat wide ribbon pasta—like a fettuccine—can replace buckwheat noodles. Black bean garlic sauce can replace the black bean mixture. Look for black bean garlic sauce, mirin, and udon noodles in the Asian section of your supermarket.

nutritional analysis

Total fat (g) 10.3	Sodium (mg) 1087	Vitamin A (RE) 1567
Fat calories (kc) 93.1	Calcium (mg) 213	Beta-carotene (RE) 9404
Cholesterol (mg) 0	Magnesium (mg) 106	Vitamin C (mg) 39
Saturated fat (g) 1.5	Zinc (mg) 1.7	Vitamin E (mg) 1.5
Polyunsaturated fat (g) 5.2	Selenium (mcg) 4	Thiamin B_1 (mg) 0.3
Monounsaturated fat (g) 2.8	Potassium (mg) 659	Riboflavin B_2 (mg) 0.2
Fiber (g) 5.5	Flavonoids (mg) 0.7	Niacin B_3 (mg) 1.5
Carbohydrates (g) 56.9	Lycopene (mg) 0	Vitamin B_6 (mg) 0.3
Sugar (g) 5.7	Fish (oz) 0	Folic acid (mcg) 84
Protein (g) 19.7	Nuts (oz) 0	Vitamin B_{12} (mcg) 0

Grilled Tuna Niçoise with Tarragon Mesclun

4 servings

Preparation time: 8 minutes

Cooking time: 10 minutes

291 calories per serving, 24% from fat

2 tablespoons olive oil

1 tablespoon coarse-grained mustard, such as Pommery or Country Dijon

3 tablespoons tarragon white wine vinegar

1 teaspoon dried tarragon

3/4 teaspoon salt

1/2 teaspoon freshly ground black pepper

4 (4-ounce) fresh tuna steaks, cut about 1/2 inch thick

1 pound small red boiling waxy potatoes

8 ounces whole fresh green beans

8 cups (10 ounces) mesclun (assorted young salad greens) or torn salad greens, loosely packed

16 grape, teardrop, or cherry tomatoes (optional)

RealAge effect if eaten 12 times a year:
A good source of protective polyunsaturated omega-3 fatty acids, and a treasure trove of monounsaturated fats, too, this recipe will make you **5.5 days younger.**

RealAge-effect ingredients:
Tuna, olive oil, green beans, salad greens, tomatoes (healthy protein, healthy fat, antioxidants, potassium, B vitamins, including folic acid and B_{12}, lycopene)

preparation: In a small bowl, combine oil, mustard, vinegar, tarragon, salt, and pepper; mix well. Brush 1 1/2 tablespoons of the mixture over tuna; set tuna and remaining dressing aside.

Rinse potatoes and green beans but do not dry. Place potatoes in an 8-inch square baking dish or microwave-safe casserole. Cover; cook at high power for 3 minutes. Add green beans; cover and continue to cook at high power 4 minutes or until vegetables are tender. Transfer to a colander and rinse with cold water to stop the cooking and cool the vegetables.

Meanwhile, heat a ridged grill pan over medium-high heat. Add tuna; cook 2 minutes per side or until seared and still very pink in center. (If a ridged grill pan is not available, tuna may be broiled 3–4 inches from heat for 3 minutes per side, or grilled outside over a bed of medium-hot coals.)

Arrange greens on four serving plates. Quarter the potatoes and cut green beans in half if large; arrange over greens. Top with tuna and drizzle with reserved dressing. Garnish with tomatoes, if desired.

substitutions: Salmon or Pacific halibut may replace tuna. White wine or champagne vinegar may replace tarragon vinegar. The result will be just a little less complex and herbal.

nutritional analysis

Total fat (g) 8.1	Sodium (mg) 556	Vitamin A (RE) 950
Fat calories (kc) 76	Calcium (mg) 94	Beta-carotene (RE) 428
Cholesterol (mg) 41.7	Magnesium (mg) 109	Vitamin C (mg) 43
Saturated fat (g) 1.3	Zinc (mg) 1.8	Vitamin E (mg) 2.67
Polyunsaturated fat (g) 2.0	Selenium (mcg) 90	Thiamin B_1 (mg) 0.5
Monounsaturated fat (g) 4.5	Potassium (mg) 1268	Riboflavin B_2 (mg) 0.5
Fiber (g) 5.3	Flavonoids (mg) 2.0	Niacin B_3 (mg) 11.6
Carbohydrates (g) 32.5	Lycopene (mg) 1.0	Vitamin B_6 (mg) 0.9
Sugar (g) 4.9	Fish (oz) 1.0	Folic acid (mcg) 184
Protein (g) 30.6	Nuts (oz) 0	Vitamin B_{12} (mcg) 9.3

Barbecued Red Snapper with Spicy Red Beans and Rice

4 servings

Preparation time: 8 minutes

Cooking time: 12 minutes

642 calories per serving, 9% from fat

RealAge effect if eaten 12 times a year:
With more RealAge-reducing omega-3s than omega-6s, serving this makes your **RealAge 11.4 days younger.**

RealAge-effect ingredients:
Vegetable juice, red snapper, kale, beans (healthy protein, healthy fat, fiber, potassium, antioxidants, B vitamins)

1/3 cup hickory barbecue sauce, such as KC Masterpiece brand

2 teaspoons Caribbean jerk seasoning mix, such as McCormick brand

1 1/2 cups spicy vegetable juice, such as Spicy V8 brand

2 cups quick-cooking brown rice, such as Uncle Ben's brand

4 (4- to 5-ounce) skinless red snapper fish fillets

3 cups packed sliced kale or collard greens

1 can (15 or 16 ounces) red beans, rinsed and drained

2 tablespoons light sour cream

preparation: Prepare charcoal or gas grill. Combine barbecue sauce and jerk seasoning; mix well. Brush 3 tablespoons of the mixture over fish; set aside.

In a small bowl, set aside 1 tablespoon of vegetable juice. In a large deep skillet, combine remaining barbecue sauce mixture, remaining vegetable juice, and 1 cup water; bring to a simmer. Stir in rice; cover and simmer 8 minutes.

Grill fish over medium-hot coals (or over medium-high heat in a ridged grill pan) 3–4 minutes per side or until fish is opaque and firm to the touch. Meanwhile, stir kale and beans into rice mixture. Cover and continue to simmer 3–4 minutes or until kale is wilted and liquid is absorbed.

Transfer rice mixture to four serving plates; top with fish. Add sour cream to reserved 1 tablespoon vegetable juice; mix well. Drizzle over fish and rice.

substitutions: Halibut or scrod may replace red snapper; Cajun or blackened seasonings may replace jerk seasoning; other cooking greens, such as mustard, may replace kale, although the taste will be sharper and not as sweet.

tips: When selecting snapper, choose firm, clear, and clean fillets that are not a bit mushy or fishy smelling.

nutritional analysis

Total fat (g) 6.5	Sodium (mg) 921	Vitamin A (RE) 908
Fat calories (kc) 58.4	Calcium (mg) 186	Beta-carotene (RE) 922
Cholesterol (mg) 49.5	Magnesium (mg) 209	Vitamin C (mg) 64.0
Saturated fat (g) 1.3	Zinc (mg) 3.6	Vitamin E (mg) 9
Polyunsaturated fat (g) 2.6	Selenium (mcg) 5	Thiamin B_1 (mg) 0.6
Monounsaturated fat (g) 2.8	Potassium (mg) 1475	Riboflavin B_2 (mg) 0.2
Fiber (g) 15.0	Flavonoids (mg) 3.2	Niacin B_3 (mg) 7.0
Carbohydrates (g) 101	Lycopene (mg) 1.6	Vitamin B_6 (mg) 1.7
Sugar (g) 9.5	Fish (oz) 4.5	Folic acid (mcg) 72
Protein (g) 42.4	Nuts (oz) 0	Vitamin B_{12} (mcg) 3.9

Golden Polenta with Exotic Mushroom Ragout

4 servings

Preparation time: 10 minutes

Cooking time: 20 minutes

274 calories per serving, 29% from fat

3 1/2 cups low-salt chicken or vegetable broth

1 cup (6 ounces) cornmeal, preferably stone-ground

2 teaspoons olive oil

1/2 cup sliced shallots or chopped yellow onion

1 1/2 cups thickly sliced carrots

2 packages (4 ounces each) mixed sliced exotic mushrooms, such as Pennsylvania Farms brand

1 1/2 cups (4 ounces) sliced button or cremini mushrooms

2 tablespoons dry sherry

1 tablespoon chopped fresh thyme or 1 teaspoon dried

3/4 teaspoon salt

1/2 teaspoon freshly ground black pepper

1/2 cup (2 ounces) crumbled herbed feta or herbed goat cheese

RealAge effect if eaten 12 times a year:
With its powerhouse of B vitamins, carotenoids from the carrots, and a little healthy fat, this soothing fall dish makes your **RealAge 4.6 days younger.**

RealAge-effect ingredients:
Olive oil, cornmeal, onions, carrots, mushrooms (B vitamins, carotenoids, potassium, healthy fats)

preparation: Combine 3 cups broth and cornmeal in a large saucepan. Mix well with a wire whisk. Bring to a simmer over medium heat, whisking occasionally. Simmer uncovered over low heat 15–18 minutes or until very thick, whisking frequently. Remove from heat; cover and keep warm.

Place a large, deep skillet over medium heat until hot. Add oil, then shallots and carrots; sauté 5 minutes. Add mushrooms; sauté 5 minutes. Add remaining 1/2 cup broth, sherry, thyme, salt, and pepper. Simmer uncovered 5 minutes or until carrots are tender, stirring occasionally.

Spread polenta over four warmed serving plates. Top with mushroom ragout and cheese. Garnish with additional chopped fresh thyme and freshly ground black pepper, if desired.

substitutions: If sliced exotic mushrooms (a combination of cremini, oyster, and shiitake mushrooms) are not available, substitute 8 ounces fresh shiitake mushrooms. Save the tough stems for stock, and slice the caps for the dish. Cubed unpeeled sweet potatoes—Garnets are some of the sweetest—can substitute for carrots.

tips: Mushroom stock—homemade or purchased—adds depth of flavor. For even more intensity, find mushroom soy sauce—I love Pearl River brand's deep, dark layers of flavor.

nutritional analysis

Total fat (g) 8.9	Sodium (mg) 782	Vitamin A (RE) 36
Fat calories (kc) 80	Calcium (mg) 89	Beta-carotene (RE) 0.4
Cholesterol (mg) 13.3	Magnesium (mg) 32	Vitamin C (mg) 6
Saturated fat (g) 2.9	Zinc (mg) 1.6	Vitamin E (mg) 0.55
Polyunsaturated fat (g) 1.0	Selenium (mcg) 0	Thiamin B_1 (mg) 0.2
Monounsaturated fat (g) 3.0	Potassium (mg) 611	Riboflavin B_2 (mg) 0.6
Fiber (g) 3.6	Flavonoids (mg) 0.7	Niacin B_3 (mg) 7.0
Carbohydrates (g) 40.6	Lycopene (mg) 0	Vitamin B_6 (mg) 0.3
Sugar (g) 2.2	Fish (oz) 0	Folic acid (mcg) 51
Protein (g) 11.9	Nuts (oz) 0	Vitamin B_{12} (mcg) 0.5

Garlicky Orzo with Spinach, Fennel, and Orange Zest

4 servings

Preparation time: 5 minutes

Cooking time: 12 minutes

218 calories per serving, 16% from fat

RealAge effect if eaten 12 times a year: 3.1 days younger.

RealAge-effect ingredients:
Garlic, olive oil, spinach, orange zest (folic acid, beta-carotene, calcium, healthy fats, flavonoids)

preparation: Heat a Dutch oven or large saucepan over medium-high heat. Add oil and garlic; cook 30 seconds. Stir in orzo; cook 30 seconds. Add broth, marjoram, fennel seeds, and pepper flakes. Simmer uncovered until orzo is tender, 7–8 minutes. Stir in spinach, tossing for 1 minute until wilted. Add salt; mix well and transfer to serving plates. Top with orange zest.

substitutions: Low-sodium beef or vegetable broth may replace chicken broth. Predictably, beef broth makes for a meatier-tasting side dish, and vegetable broth gives a cleaner flavor.

tips: Crushing fennel seeds (and, actually, almost any seed) brings the aromatic oils to the surface and provides extra flavors. Don't toast these seeds, however, as their delicate perfume will evaporate. Orange zest brightens the dish, adding color and a touch of sweet sourness. If you don't have an orange, don't fret; any citrus fruit will do. Use a low-sodium broth so you control the salt content. A touch of red pepper flakes adds zing. If the dish seems to be missing a little something, use 1/2 rather than 1/4 teaspoon of flakes.

2 teaspoons garlic-infused or extra-virgin olive oil

6 garlic cloves, minced

1 cup (6 ounces) orzo (a rice-shaped pasta), uncooked

2 cups low-salt chicken broth

1 teaspoon dried marjoram

3/4 teaspoon fennel seeds, slightly crushed

1/4 teaspoon crushed red pepper flakes

1 package (10 ounces) spinach leaves, sliced, or baby spinach leaves

1 1/4 teaspoons salt

2 teaspoons freshly shredded orange zest

nutritional analysis

Total fat (g) 4.0	Sodium (mg) 841	Vitamin A (RE) 479
Fat calories (kc) 36	Calcium (mg) 86	Beta-carotene (RE) 2860
Cholesterol (mg) 14.7	Magnesium (mg) 66	Vitamin C (mg) 23
Saturated fat (g) 0.6	Zinc (mg) 0.80	Vitamin E (mg) 1.7
Polyunsaturated fat (g) 0.6	Selenium (mcg) 5	Thiamin B_1 (mg) 0.16
Monounsaturated fat (g) 2.0	Potassium (mg) 533	Riboflavin B_2 (mg) 0.24
Fiber (g) 2.4	Flavonoids (mg) 0.7	Niacin B_3 (mg) 2.7
Carbohydrates (g) 15.4	Lycopene (mg) 0	Vitamin B_6 (mg) 0.2
Sugar (g) 0.4	Fish (oz) 0	Folic acid (mcg) 144
Protein (g) 7.0	Nuts (oz) 0	Vitamin B_{12} (mcg) 0.2

Chocolate Strawberry Sundae

4 servings

Preparation time: 5 minutes

216 calories per serving, 10% from fat

4 (1/2-cup) scoops nonfat or low-fat chocolate frozen yogurt

1 1/2 cups sliced strawberries

1 cup low-fat granola cereal, such as Quaker brand

2 teaspoons confectioners' sugar

RealAge effect if eaten 12 times a year:
Berries of all kinds are powerhouses of fiber. That plus the flavonoids in chocolate make your **RealAge 7.2 days younger.**

RealAge-effect ingredients:
Strawberries, whole-grain granola (fiber, flavonoids)

preparation: Scoop yogurt into four serving bowls; top with strawberries and granola. Place confectioners' sugar in a strainer and shake over sundaes.

substitutions: One cup whole-grain cereal flakes may replace the granola.

Coffee-flavored frozen yogurt may replace the chocolate frozen yogurt, and blueberries may replace the strawberries (a chocolate blueberry sundae).

tips: For a special occasion, drizzle a bit of Baileys Irish Cream (a cream liqueur) or chocolate liqueur over the sundae just before serving. The confectioners' sugar brightens the color of the dessert; just 1/2 teaspoon per serving is all that's needed. For color, place all the strawberries on top. If you can find them, get the tiny alpine strawberries instead. Nuggets of berry goodness, they still grow wild, and can be found in farmers' markets.

nutritional analysis

Total fat (g) 2	Sodium (mg) 107	Vitamin A (RE) 299
Fat calories (kc) 87	Calcium (mg) 232	Beta-carotene (RE) 20
Cholesterol (mg) 1.4	Magnesium (mg) 115	Vitamin C (mg) 41
Saturated fat (g) 0.49	Zinc (mg) 3.9	Vitamin E (mg) 3.3
Polyunsaturated fat (g) 2.3	Selenium (mcg) 21	Thiamin B_1 (mg) 0.6
Monounsaturated fat (g) 5.0	Potassium (mg) 588	Riboflavin B_2 (mg) 0.8
Fiber (g) 8.4	Flavonoids (mg) 1.9	Niacin B_3 (mg) 5.3
Carbohydrates (g) 12.8	Lycopene (mg) 0	Vitamin B_6 (mg) 0.5
Sugar (g) 26.7	Fish (oz) 0	Folic acid (mcg) 94
Protein (g) 15.7	Nuts (oz) 0	Vitamin B_{12} (mcg) 0.9

Succulent Ripe Berry Parfait

4 servings

Preparation time: 15 minutes

245 calories per serving, 9% from fat

RealAge effect if eaten 12 times a year:
Blueberries, raspberries, and strawberries have incredibly high antioxidant capacities—and they're delicious, to boot. This parfait will make your **RealAge 8.4 days younger.**

RealAge-effect ingredients:
Berries, nuts, yogurt, melon, whole-grain cereal, soy yogurt (antioxidants, calcium, healthy protein, magnesium, selenium, potassium, vitamin B$_3$, folic acid, flavonoids, fiber)

24 ounces low-fat soy vanilla yogurt, such as White Wave brand

4 teaspoons honey

1/2 teaspoon pure vanilla extract

1 cup hulled, quartered strawberries

1 cup raspberries

1 cup blueberries

1 cup diced honeydew melon

1/2 cup Grape-Nuts (or similar) cereal

preparation: In a medium bowl, combine yogurt, honey, and vanilla; mix well. In four large goblets or clear dessert dishes, arrange fruit and yogurt mixture in four layers. Top with cereal.

substitutions: Low-fat vanilla yogurt may replace soy yogurt, blackberries may replace blueberries, and cantaloupe may replace honeydew melon.

tips: Look for especially juicy melon—its ripeness will help sweeten the dish. The crunch of the cereal is a chef's way to keep you interested: The rough texture contrasts with the smoothness of the yogurt and the firm flesh of the fruit to make your mouth go "Wow!" Keep the melon diced medium: it's easier to eat small chunks rather than big ones, and the melon will go further.

nutritional analysis

Total fat (g) 4.0	Sodium (mg) 128	Vitamin A (RE) 203
Fat calories (kc) 36	Calcium (mg) 30	Beta-carotene (RE) 95
Cholesterol (mg) 0	Magnesium (mg) 58	Vitamin C (mg) 44
Saturated fat (g) 0.4	Zinc (mg) 1.0	Vitamin E (mg) 0.3
Polyunsaturated fat (g) 1.7	Selenium (mcg) 6	Thiamin B$_1$ (mg) 0.5
Monounsaturated fat (g) 0.7	Potassium (mg) 561	Riboflavin B$_2$ (mg) 0.4
Fiber (g) 6.6	Flavonoids (mg) 1.1	Niacin B$_3$ (mg) 3.6
Carbohydrates (g) 36	Lycopene (mg) 0	Vitamin B$_6$ (mg) 0.4
Sugar (g) 16.7	Fish (oz) 0	Folic acid (mcg) 70
Protein (g) 7.6	Nuts (oz) 0	Vitamin B$_{12}$ (mcg) 0.8

Sweet Baked Apples with Cherries

4 servings

Preparation time: 2 minutes

Cooking time: 18 minutes

105 calories per serving, 5% from fat

2 large baking apples, such as Rome Beauty

1 1/4 cups apple juice, preferably unfiltered organic juice

1/2 cup (2 ounces) dried pitted cherries

1/4 teaspoon ground cloves

2 seedless clementines or tangerines, peeled, separated into segments

Mint sprigs *(optional)*

RealAge effect if eaten 12 times a year:
A great natural source of vitamin A, citrus fruits add freshness, sprightliness, and extra minerals, too, making your **RealAge 1.1 days younger.**

RealAge-effect ingredients:
Apples, cherries, tangerines, apple juice (fiber, antioxidants, flavonoids, potassium)

preparation: Heat oven to 400°F. Cut apples in half; cut out and discard core, seeds, and stems. Place 1/4 cup of the apple juice in an 8-inch baking dish or casserole. Place apples cut sides down over juice. Bake 15–18 minutes or until apples are tender.

Meanwhile, simmer remaining 1 cup apple juice in a small saucepan over medium-high heat 5 minutes. Add cherries and cloves; reduce heat and simmer uncovered 10 minutes, or until cherries are plumped, stirring occasionally. Remove from heat; stir in citrus sections.

Arrange apple halves, cut sides up, on serving dishes. Pour any remaining liquid from dish into cherry mixture and spoon the mixture over apples. Garnish with mint sprigs, if desired.

substitutions: Dried cranberries may replace cherries. Baking apples cook more quickly and develop a softer texture when baked than eating apples. McIntosh apples are another good choice for this recipe.

tips: A little ground clove goes a long way; its zippiness is a perfect complement to this fall/winter dessert. Try studding each apple with two whole cloves, so that they are submerged in the apple juice as the apples bake. Remove the cloves before eating the apple, which will now be scented with zingy spice.

nutritional analysis

Total fat (g) 0.5	Sodium (mg) 6	Vitamin A (RE) 45
Fat calories (kc) 4.8	Calcium (mg) 18	Beta-carotene (RE) 273
Cholesterol (mg) 0	Magnesium (mg) 13	Vitamin C (mg) 18
Saturated fat (g) 0.1	Zinc (mg) 0.2	Vitamin E (mg) 0.4
Polyunsaturated fat (g) 0.2	Selenium (mcg) 2	Thiamin B_1 (mg) 0.1
Monounsaturated fat (g) 0.1	Potassium (mg) 272	Riboflavin B_2 (mg) 0.04
Fiber (g) 2.8	Flavonoids (mg) 3.9	Niacin B_3 (mg) 0.2
Carbohydrates (g) 26.4	Lycopene (mg) 0	Vitamin B_6 (mg) 0.1
Sugar (g) 22.8	Fish (oz) 0	Folic acid (mcg) 11
Protein (g) 0.7	Nuts (oz) 0	Vitamin B_{12} (mcg) 0

Roasted Pears with Raspberry Coulis, Chocolate, and Pistachios

4 servings

Preparation time: 3 minutes

Cooking time: 27 minutes

172 calories per serving, 27.3% from fat

RealAge effect if eaten 12 times a year: Can chocolate make you younger? You bet—as long as it is real (cocoa-based) chocolate and you eat it first! The RA factor for this delicious bit of paradise: **at least 2.6 days younger.**
RealAge-effect ingredients:
Pears, grape juice, berries, pistachios, chocolate (antioxidants, healthy fats, potassium, fiber)

2 large Bartlett, Comice, or Anjou pears, preferably red

1 cup white grape juice, such as Welch's brand

1 package (12 ounces) frozen unsweetened raspberries, thawed, or 2 cups fresh raspberries

2 tablespoons mini-chocolate chips (from cocoa—real chocolate, not milk chocolate)

3 tablespoons coarsely chopped pistachios, toasted

Mint sprigs (optional)

preparation: Heat oven to 400°F. Cut each pear in half; remove core with a melon baller or metal measuring teaspoon. Arrange pears, cut sides down, in a shallow baking dish. Pour grape juice over pears. Bake 18–20 minutes or until pears are tender when pierced with the tip of a paring knife.

Meanwhile, puree raspberries in food processor; strain and discard seeds. Transfer roasted pears to serving plates, cut sides up; sprinkle chocolate chips over the pears (the heat of the pears will melt the chips). Combine pureed raspberries and liquid remaining in baking dish in a small saucepan. Cook over high heat until sauce has reduced to 3/4 cup, 6–8 minutes. Spoon sauce over and around pears; sprinkle with pistachios and garnish with mint sprigs, if desired.

substitutions: If you have champagne or white wine and not white grape juice, then use it without fear, and with a teaspoon of sugar. Sliced toasted almonds or chopped hazelnuts may replace pistachios, and blackberries or strawberries may replace raspberries.

nutritional analysis

Total fat (g) 5.2	Sodium (mg) 7	Vitamin A (RE) 14
Fat calories (kc) 47	Calcium (mg) 45	Beta-carotene (RE) 50
Cholesterol (mg) 0	Magnesium (mg) 32	Vitamin C (mg) 15
Saturated fat (g) 1.4	Zinc (mg) 0.4	Vitamin E (mg) 0.9
Polyunsaturated fat (g) 0.7	Selenium (mcg) 2	Thiamin B_1 (mg) 0.1
Monounsaturated fat (g) 2.6	Potassium (mg) 344	Riboflavin B_2 (mg) 0.1
Fiber (g) 4.9	Flavonoids (mg) 0	Niacin B_3 (mg) 0.7
Carbohydrates (g) 31.8	Lycopene (mg) 0	Vitamin B_6 (mg) 0.15
Sugar (g) 24.0	Fish (oz) 0	Folic acid (mcg) 24
Protein (g) 2.7	Nuts (oz) 0.2	Vitamin B_{12} (mcg) 0

Maple Cranberry-Topped Frozen Yogurt

4 servings

Preparation time: 5 minutes

Cooking time: 8 minutes

193 calories per serving, 5% from fat

1 cup fresh or frozen cranberries

1 cup orange juice

1/2 cup dried cranberries

3 tablespoons pure maple syrup

1 1/3 cups low-fat vanilla frozen yogurt

1 teaspoon finely shredded orange peel

RealAge effect if eaten 12 times a year:
Low in saturated fat, this dish still tastes like a million bucks and takes **2.6 days off your RealAge.**

RealAge-effect ingredients:
Cranberries, orange juice, orange peel (flavonoids, antioxidants, folic acid, calcium, potassium)

preparation: Combine fresh or frozen cranberries, orange juice, and dried cranberries in a medium saucepan. Bring to a boil over high heat. Reduce heat; simmer uncovered 7–8 minutes or until cranberries are popped and sauce thickens slightly. Remove from heat; stir in syrup. Serve warm, at room temperature, or chilled over frozen yogurt. Garnish with orange peel.

substitutions: Coffee frozen yogurt may replace the vanilla, and dried cherries may replace the cranberries. If you use coffee frozen yogurt and can find a great-tasting brand, you can use its fat-free version; if you use vanilla, however, choose the 1%-fat variety instead of the fat-free version.

tips: Splashing 2 teaspoons of Cointreau, Grand Marnier, or triple sec over the top adds an elegant touch of orange-flavored liqueur. Try any or all. Combining fresh and dried fruit is an easy way to double flavor: Fresh fruit always has more juiciness, and dried fruit always has more sweetness. Together, they pack a flavor wallop.

nutritional analysis

Total fat (g) 1.1	Sodium (mg) 77	Vitamin A (RE) 31
Fat calories (kc) 10	Calcium (mg) 141	Beta-carotene (RE) 107
Cholesterol (mg) 4.2	Magnesium (mg) 22	Vitamin C (mg) 39
Saturated fat (g) 0.7	Zinc (mg) 0.7	Vitamin E (mg) 0.03
Polyunsaturated fat (g) 0.2	Selenium (mcg) 3	Thiamin B_1 (mg) 0.1
Monounsaturated fat (g) 0.4	Potassium (mg) 332	Riboflavin B_2 (mg) 0.2
Fiber (g) 1.7	Flavonoids (mg) 10.7	Niacin B_3 (mg) 0.5
Carbohydrates (g) 30.1	Lycopene (mg) 0	Vitamin B_6 (mg) 0.1
Sugar (g) 22.2	Fish (oz) 0	Folic acid (mcg) 45
Protein (g) 4.4	Nuts (oz) 0	Vitamin B_{12} (mcg) 0.4

Triple Apple Sauté

4 servings

Preparation time: 12 minutes

Cooking time: 12 minutes

199 calories per serving,
10% from fat

RealAge effect if eaten 12 times a year:
With blood pressure–reducing potassium and hefty amounts of fiber and isoflavones, all underlined by monounsaturated oil, this RealAge-reducer weighs in at **2.9 days younger.**

RealAge-effect ingredients:
Apples, nuts, apple juice (potassium, fiber, isoflavones, flavonoids, healthy fat)

3 large or 4 small cooking apples, such as Ambrosia or Jonagold (1 1/2 pounds)

1/4 cup apple butter

1/4 cup unsweetened apple juice or cider

1/2 teaspoon five-spice powder *(see tips)*

1/4 cup chopped Brazil nuts or walnuts, toasted

1/2 cup nonfat or low-fat vanilla frozen yogurt, such as Häagen-Dazs

preparation: Cut apples into quarters; discard stems, core, and seeds. Cut apple quarters into thin slices. Heat a large nonstick skillet over medium-high heat until hot. Add apples; cook until apples begin to brown, about 4 minutes, tossing occasionally. Stir in apple butter, apple juice, and five-spice powder; continue to cook 5–8 minutes or until apples are tender and sauce thickens, tossing frequently. Transfer to serving plates; top with nuts. Serve with frozen yogurt.

substitutions: One-half teaspoon cinnamon may be substituted for the five-spice powder; the flavor will be softer and sweeter.

tips: Five-spice powder is a combination of Chinese spices that usually includes cinnamon, cloves, fennel seed, star anise, and Szechwan peppercorns. Look for the spice mix in the Asian section of your supermarket or by the other spices.

As the apples brown and caramelize in the pan, their own natural sugars add to the rich sauce.

nutritional analysis

Total fat (g) 2.3	Sodium (mg) 21	Vitamin A (RE) 29
Fat calories (kc) 20	Calcium (mg) 62	Beta-carotene (RE) 16
Cholesterol (mg) 1.1	Magnesium (mg) 27	Vitamin C (mg) 6
Saturated fat (g) 0.3	Zinc (mg) 0.4	Vitamin E (mg) 0.51
Polyunsaturated fat (g) 0.9	Selenium (mcg) 4	Thiamin B_1 (mg) 0.1
Monounsaturated fat (g) 0.4	Potassium (mg) 403	Riboflavin B_2 (mg) 0.1
Fiber (g) 7.3	Flavonoids (mg) 5.1	Niacin B_3 (mg) 0.5
Carbohydrates (g) 62	Lycopene (mg) 0	Vitamin B_6 (mg) 0.2
Sugar (g) 34.8	Fish (oz) 0	Folic acid (mcg) 7
Protein (g) 4.1	Nuts (oz) 0.3	Vitamin B_{12} (mcg) 0